C000065195

# Summary Bundle: Biography & Success | Readtrepreneur Publishing: Includes Summary of Hamilton & Summary of Head Strong

## ABBEY BEATHAN

**Text Copyright © ABBEY BEATHAN**

All rights reserved. No part of this guide may be reproduced in any form without permission in writing from the publisher except in the case of brief quotations embodied in critical articles or reviews.

## Legal & Disclaimer

The information contained in this book is not designed to replace or take the place of any form of medicine or professional medical advice. The information in this book has been provided for educational and entertainment purposes only.

The information contained in this book has been compiled from sources deemed reliable, and it is accurate to the best of the Author's knowledge; however, the Author cannot guarantee its accuracy and validity and cannot be held liable for any errors or omissions. Changes are periodically made to this book. You must consult your doctor or get professional medical advice before using any of the suggested remedies, techniques, or information in this book. Images used in this book are not the same as of that of the actual book. This is a totally separate and different entity from that of the original book titled: Hamilton: The Revolution"

Upon using the information contained in this book, you agree to hold harmless the Author from and against any damages, costs, and expenses, including any legal fees potentially resulting from the application of any of the information provided by this guide. This disclaimer applies to any damages or injury caused by the use and application, whether directly or indirectly, of any advice or information presented, whether for breach of contract, tort, negligence, personal injury, criminal intent, or under any other cause of action.

You agree to accept all risks of using the information presented inside this book. You need to consult a professional medical practitioner in order to ensure you are both able and healthy enough to participate in this program.

# Table of Contents

# The Book at a Glance

With eleven Tony Awards that include Best Musical, *Hamilton: An American Musical* managed to fuse hip hop, rnb, pop, and traditional Broadway tunes while smashing cultural boundaries *and* bridging the gap between today's diverse generation and America's history all at the same time.

**HAMILTON: THE REVOLUTION** provides an in-depth account of the long and arduous process to creating one of Broadway's smash hits, from the conception of the idea to use rap as a storytelling tool (a mixtape experiment tested in the White House Poetry Jam, no less), to the show's opening night at the Public Theater in New York six years later, and the aftermath of what would be one of the biggest defining moments in American theater.

Written by *Hamilton*'s creator, Tony award winner Lin-Manuel Miranda, and cultural critic and artist Jeremy McCarter, each chapter of the book alludes to each stage of the creation of the musical and the individuals who played a major role in the show's success, both on and off the stage.

As Hamilton's complete libretto, each chapter also includes Miranda's exhaustive footnotes on each of the 48 songs in both acts of the play, highlighting each track's inspiration, references to historical and modern figures, as well as personal anecdotes from the author himself.

Act 1 of the book features 16 chapters centered on the historical basis of Lin-Manuel's brainchild, sparked by that fateful vacation in which he picked up a copy of historian Ron Chernow's biography of founding father Alexander Hamilton, as well as the sketches of the key people in the musical's creation and execution—from Miranda's own 'cabinet,' consisting of theater director Tommy Kail, and orchestrator Alex Lacamoire, to producer Jeffrey Seller, Public Theater head Oskar Eustis, choreographer Andy Blankenbuehler, designer Paul Tazewell, and some of the lead actors and actresses from the original Broadway Cast (Chris Jackson, Leslie Odom, Jr., Renée Elsie Goldsberry, and Phillipa Soo). There are also dedicated chapters to some of *Hamilton's* hip hop musical inspirations, from Ja Rule to Mobb Deep and Biggie Smalls. A snippet of Miranda's personal life is also highlighted, as his son Sebastian 'makes his debut' in the midst of the *Hamilton* preparations.

Act 2 includes 16 chapters presenting the rest of the original cast leads (Oak Onaodowan, Daveed Diggs, Jasmine Cephas Jones, Jonathan Groff, and Anthony Ramos), as well as a chapter on Howell Binkley's stage and lighting design for the show. The authors also present discussions on how the musical itself reflects the current issues surrounding the

11

nation's politics—from using a rap battle-style format during cabinet meetings, to showcasing controversies and political downfalls caused by indiscretions and character flaw.

In a chapter, Miranda tells about how one colleague's loss deepened the meaning behind one of the songs that also spoke of the grief when Hamilton's son passed, paving the way for healing through music. The last chapters told of the struggles of completing a full-scale, two-act musical to meet a business deadline, finally reaching the opening night, and reveling on the show's massive success and unforgettable moments—including a visit from President Barack Obama.

*Hamilton: A Revolution* also features the photographic work of celebrated photographers Frank Ockenfels and Joan Marcus, with exclusive cast portraits and scenes from *Hamilton: an American Musical.*

# Introduction, or Plan of the Work

Former *New York* magazine drama critic Jeremy McCarter writes about how the love for both Broadway and hip hop brought him and Lin-Manuel Miranda together, specifically after his raving review of Miranda's first show, *In the Heights*.

McCarter reminisces the first time he had seen what he had been longing to see in Broadway—stories told using rap and hip hop—when he came and saw the play, and that night in 2008 when Miranda first spoke to him of his desire to put together a hip hop mixtape album featuring the life of one of America's founding fathers, Alexander Hamilton.

When McCarter joined the Public Theater in 2011, he got together with its artistic director Oskar Eustis proposed Lin-Manuel's idea not as an album, but as a musical show.

With producer Jeffrey Seller on board two years later, *Hamilton* began to develop and on its very opening night in 2015, Miranda came to him with the idea of writing a book with him.

McCarter identifies two stories of revolution in this book: first, the 18th Century American Revolution, the backdrop of Alexander Hamilton's life, and second, the revolution of the

Broadway show itself, throughout the six years that it took to write, develop, and prepare.

In his collection of interviews, personal accounts, emails, meetings, social media entries, workshops, and dressing-room hangouts, McCarter yields three large surprises about the show: 1) that *Hamilton*, while it looks seamless, effortless, and inevitable, was anything but; 2) that its creation amplifies the show's themes, such as how stories are told become history itself; and 3) that Lin-Manuel Miranda's one-man accomplishment as composer, lyricist, librettist, and star of the show is realized by dozens of gifted individuals who came together from different backgrounds, and this kind of unification not only celebrates Hamilton's life, it continues the revolution and adds to his legacy.

# ACT I

## Chapter 1: On the Origins of Revolution, Both National & Musical, with Reference to Opening Numbers & White House Raps

This chapter is an account of Lin-Manuel's night at the White House' program, "An Evening of Poetry, Music, and the Spoken Word," where he surprised the distinguished guests—an audience that included James Earl Jones, Esperanza Spalding, and novelist Michael Chabon, not to mention the President, Barack Obama, and First Lady Michelle Obama—by introducing his piece as an excerpt from a hip hop album he was working on, based on the life of the former Treasury Secretary and founding father Alexander Hamilton.

His performance of the song, "Alexander Hamilton," with Alex Lacamoire's piano accompaniment, earned Miranda a standing ovation that night and over a million views as the video went viral on YouTube.

The song was a refresher course on the life of the orphaned, destitute Caribbean kid who came to another country, built a life for himself, and in turn, helped build a nation. It serves as a prototype for the millions of immigrants who are shaping today's America, including that child born from a Kenyan father and a mother from Kansas, who would later on become the President of the United States, The Puerto Rican son from New York who would create the show that revolutionizes Broadway, and the musical genius from Jamaica who would push the show forward with his sound creations.

## *"Alexander Hamilton"*

The first song in the musical is an establishing shot of the life of America's first Treasury Secretary. Lin-Manuel's footnotes on the lyrics started with the opening piano riff, which he likened to a door slamming shut.

"Alexander Hamilton" was first meant to be a monologue for the character of Aaron Burr, but as the mixtape concept became a musical show, Miranda looked into the prologue of *Sweeney Todd* and had those who witnessed Hamilton's life come together to set the stage for the protagonist's entrance. The song tells the audience how he survived the hurricane that devastated his home, how he doubled down on coming to America and getting his education and climbing his way up in life and in politics. It also give small snapshots of how the other characters played a role in his success, failures, and eventually, death.

# Chapter 2: In Which Tommy Kail is Introduced, and His Adventures with Lin Surveyed

Thomas Kail, *Hamilton*'s director and Lin-Manuel's close friend and musical confidant, played a vital role in pushing for the development of the show itself. Two years after the viral White House performance, the Hamilton mixtape project had made no progress, save for a second song that had been sitting unfinished in Miranda's notebooks.

Kail's history with Miranda started way back when he first started his theater company after graduating from school. A friend recommended that he produce Lin's show, and on June 2002, they met to discuss the plans for what would be the Tony award-winning *In the Heights*.

When the founders of Ars Nova, a theater in the West Side of Manhattan, invited Lin's rap group Freestyle Love Supreme (which Tommy is also the director of) to perform in their annual benefit on June 2011, what would turn out to be *Hamilton's* I-want song, "My Shot," made its unofficial debut. The enthusiastic response from the audience drove Kail to urge Lin to start seriously developing the project.

To expedite the advancement of their venture on Hamilton,

Tommy proposed that they write enough material so they can present a concert version of the songs within six months. The venue, as they found out later on, would be the Lincoln Center, where Lin was invited to perform for the American Songbook concert series. They were set to perform on the 11th of January—Alexander Hamilton's birthday, as fate would have it.

### *"Aaron Burr, Sir"*

Lin emphasizes in his footnotes for this particular song that the way Hamilton and Aaron Burr met in the show was fictional—and that Hamilton's punching incident with the bursar was a historical leap, much to Chernow's chagrin.

They didn't meet John Laurens, Hercules Mulligan, and Marquis de Lafayette for the first time at the Fraunces Tavern (which still exists to this day), either—the scene allowed for the song's rap circle that establishes each character's brief history and personality, and how they view the war.

Miranda also notes that the closing line of the song, "If you stand for nothing, Burr, what do you fall for?" was referenced from a line that was made by a different Hamilton and not the founding father, but was still used because of how it encapsulates Burr's malleable stand on issues.

## *"My Shot"*

The show's I-want song is a fast-paced where he makes his lifelong friends in Laurens, Mulligan, and Lafayette, as well as Burr. Lin notes how the song was laden with little snippets of homages and allusions to his hip hop influences woven into the bars and lines (Tupac's "Holla if you hear me," the way Notorious B.I.G. spelled his own name in "Going Back to Cali", and samples of Busta Rhyme's "Pass the Courvoisier," which was later on revised due to potential copyright problems).

Miranda tells the characters' backgrounds via differentiating their tones, rap speed, accents, and ideals about why their joined the rebellion. Burr comes in during the later part to provide a cold dose of reality, however, and it drives Hamilton to voice out in fast-paced, tongue-twisting lyrics that took Lin years to complete—it was a picture of how Hamilton's brain thinks, and he wanted to reflect the urgency and passion that translates to words that flow out quickly and without second thought.

This cements the characters' friendship and determination to fight the war together.

# Chapter 3: Giving the History of Ron Chernow, Along with Remarks on Who May Play a Founding Father

After Lin returned from his vacation in Mexico, having read Ron Chernow's *Alexander Hamilton*, he reached out to the author and invited him to see *In the Heights*. He immediately asked Chernow to be the historical consultant for the Hamilton project.

However, there wasn't much historical material to pore over that was not already in Chernow's book. Lin wanted to know little accurate details about Hamilton—if he smoked, what he did with his hands, if Washington would have seen him as a younger version of himself—and the author had encouraged him to fill in the gaps with creative content.

Miranda's imagination went beyond writing in the characters' little idiosyncrasies. Ron admitted to being "shocked" when he came in at Lin's invitation to watch actors sing through the first act of the show; the artists to play Hamilton, Washington, Burr, Laurens, Mulligan, Lafayette, and other key characters were black and Latino.

This, however, sets the tone for the show's principle that *Hamilton* was "a story about America then, told by America now."

Chernow became a "militant defender" of this principle, but still had something to say about the historical inconsistencies in the songs—something that Miranda firmly defended. The poetic liberties he took when creating fictional initial meetings for the characters not only put the characters together all at once, it also emphasized the coherence of their motivation to fight the war, end slavery, as well as inaugurate their friendship.

## *"The Story of Tonight"*

Lin wrote the melody for this song when he was 16 (formerly titled, "I've Got a Bridge to Sell You"), and conveys the underlying innocence and even the yearning of four young men who found friends to sing a melody with while drinking.

"The Story of Tonight" became a theme that returns in various parts of the show as the four characters reflect on different events of their lives, based on Sondheim's *Merrily We Roll Along,* where the three friends also sing a line repeatedly ("Here's to us; who's like us? Damn Few").

# Chapter 4: In Which the Character of New York City is Considered in Its Musical and Scenic Aspects, by Reference to David Korins and a Curious Episode of Historical Vertigo

New York City holds a dear place in Lin-Manuel's heart, as it did in Hamilton's. While the other founding fathers were, for the most part, country boys who preferred the tranquility of rural farming estates, Alexander immigrated straight to the bustling city. It reflected his very mind and manner of speaking: fast, non-stop, and very volatile.

The show shifts its center to the city when the three Schuyler sisters—Angelica, Eliza, and Peggy—are introduced, sneaking out against their father's orders to check out the happenings in the square.

The depiction of how New York looked like in the late 1700s was the challenge that David Korins took on, listening to Lin's many demos and visiting sites such as the Fraunces Tavern and the Morris-Jumel Mansion (Washington's headquarters during the war) to find inspiration for the stage design.

The set design became a transforming construction site—the

way carpenters from New York and other coastline cities built them in the 18th century with heavy influences that stem from their shipbuilding and masonry.

## *"The Schuyler Sisters"*

Lin-Manuel calls "The Schuyler Sisters" *Hamilton's* "One Short Day in Emerald City." It introduces the three ladies in a context outside of the time they met Alexander Hamilton, and the city that serves as a backdrop for most of the life-changing turns of events throughout the story.

The song pays homage to both Jay Z and Pharell in a little detail in Burr's promptly-rejected advances towards Angelica ("Excuse me, miss"), and establishes her intelligent, strong personality as the oldest Schuyler sister, with mentions of reading "Common Sense," and wanting to meet Jefferson so she could "compel him to include women in the sequel."

# Chapter 5: Stakes is High; Or, What Happened at Lincoln Center and What Came After, Including Lunch with Jeffrey Seller

Producer Jeffrey Seller was there on January 11, 2012, among 450 audience members who came to see Lin-Manuel perform 12 songs from the Hamilton Project. Everyone, including him, was left baffled and excited for more—and for the most part, nobody knew if the tracks were for a mixtape, a concept album, or a show. But Seller was convinced that it was meant to be part of a Broadway musical, and he invited Miranda to lunch and offered to produce the play a few weeks later.

Hailing from Oak Park in Detroit, Seller's first experience with theater was his synagogue's Purim play that "set the Queen Esther's story to the score of *South Pacific*." Since then, he had dabbled in playwriting and acting, but found his true calling: staging, promoting, and raising money for shows. He moved to New York after college, and in the mid-90s, produced his first musical with Kevin McCollum, *Rent*. It was soon followed by the puppet musical *Avenue Q,* and later on, *In the Heights*—all of which won a Tony for Best Musical. He formed *Adventureland*, his own company as a solo producer in 2012, with *Hamilton* as its first project.

## *"Farmer Refuted"*

From the very beginning, *Hamilton* was set to change people's perception about Broadway, and what theater should look and sound like. Lin emphasizes that "theater is a mongrel art form," the same way America's backbone is comprised of immigrants. The show aims to inject hip hop into Broadway, the way jazz and rock permeated the traditional plays—and this heavy and concentrated fusion is evident even as early as the first act.

"Farmer Refuted," Hamilton's battle of ideals with British loyalist Samuel Seabury, combines the jaunty tunes of drums, fifes, and harpsichord with fast-paced hip hop bars that match the melodic lyrics in every rhyme—reminiscent of Joell Ortiz' homage to Puerto Rican MC Big Pun. Hamilton ripped Seabury's pro-Brit lines to pieces by rapping over him, using the same waltz tempo and cadences—one could say he was showing off his oratory skills in this scene.

# Chapter 6: On the Orchestrating Techniques of Alex Lacamoire, with Lively Appearances by Van Halen, Elmo, and an Actual Beatle

As choreographer Andy Blankenbuehler put it, "Lin will have an amazing inspiration and put it forward in a way that you know exactly where he's driving, and Alex will pave the street."

Alex Lacamoire, *Hamilton's* musical director and orchestrator, is the one person who translates Lin's rudimentary arrangements and demos into notated music to be played by the band. Songs are meant to be reworked and revised over and over, and the push-and-pull dynamic of Lacamoire and Miranda transformed rough recordings of rap and chords with sampled beats and sounds from Logic Pro into sheets and sheets of keys and sharps and flats.

Alex first worked with Lin in *In the Heights*, where he was recommended by an actor friend—a gig that would land him his first Tony Award. He started playing the piano at age 4 and kept playing, even after being diagnosed with a hearing disability. His musical talents also encompass composing and songwriting, though with friends like Lin-Manuel and Tommy Kitt, he insists that there's no point bothering if it's not going to be as good as theirs. He does, however, write children's songs for shows such as *Sesame Street*.

## *"You'll be Back"*

"You'll Be Back," is yet another result of Lin and Alex' back and forth swing of interpreting what they write and finding the right combination of Miranda's simple approach to Lacamoire's own construal of what it sound and feel like.

This particular song, with its title line coming from actor Hugh Laurie while drinking with Lin, is a love letter (and not so subtle warning) from King George to the rebelling American colonists, had a cheery and romantic melody that needed something more than the usual harpsichord that projects the royalty singing it. It did, however, sound like a different kind of British royalty—the Beatles.

This led to injecting an homage to the legendary band's "Getting Better" and "Penny Lane," as well as "Being for the Benefit of Mr. Kite." The result: a tuneful earful laced with sociopathy and humor.

Both Lin and Alex got a personal nod from Sir Paul McCartney himself, who praised the show's vocal harmonies when he came to watch *Hamilton* during its early days at the Public Theater.

# Chapter 7: On the Character of George Washington and the Character of Chris Jackson

George Washington's character in *Hamilton* was as commanding as the real man himself—his character rapped in a metronomic, measured pace, had an authoritative aura that demanded respect, yet desperate to save his men from the grips of what seemed to be a losing war.

Lin-Manuel saw the personification of this character in rapper Common—and in a closer candidate, his *In the Heights* co-star Chris Jackson. His strong, athletic stature, his powerhouse voice that could belt out R&B tunes, and how, as Miranda put it, he "is so sure of his instrument and has this kind of moral authority onstage" made him the first choice for "G-Dubs" (as Tommy called Chris).

The parallels between the two pairs, Hamilton and Washington, and Miranda and Jackson, also cemented the perfect chemistry for the roles. Alexander and Lin were both verbose, passionate, and loud, while George and Chris were more subdued, taller, and more reserved. Their friendship and interactions come to play in both Broadway and in their performances in Freestyle Love Supreme, in which Jackson joined later on.

## *"Right Hand Man"*

This song marks the introduction of a pivotal character in *Hamilton*: George Washington. Starting from Alexander's musings about wishing for a war to help him rise from poverty, the track aims to provide a sense of insecurity—something that takes away the predictability of the 18th Century Revolution and provides a look at what goes on in the mind of then Commander Washington as his men fight to stay alive.

It also showcases Hamilton's ingenuous efforts to contribute to the rebellion and his thirst for battlefield glory (going as far as stealing cannons from the British forces with Mulligan). This is where he gets Washington's attention and, to Alexander's dismay, appoints him as his right hand man—a position that Burr had offered to take. This is the start of his long and heated rivalry with Hamilton.

# Chapter 8: Concerning the Lady and the Tramp, in Olden Days and Our Own, with Reference to "Helpless" and Many Songs That Feature Ja Rule

Alexander and Eliza's courtship was itching to be told—she was a rich, sophisticated and well-born; he was an orphaned bastard who became a soldier to rise from poverty. But after a month of whirlwind courtship, they were engaged.

The show, if done in the traditional Broadway manner, would "be brimming with waltz and ballads—but Lin took a different, if not better avenue: rap and R&B.

Taking his cue from partnering hip hop artists with female singers (i.e., Method Man and Mary J. Blige, Ja Rule and Ashanti), he wrote the Hamilton-Schuyler romance saga in an upbeat song reminiscent of Beyoncé and Jay Z's "Crazy in Love."

### *"A Winter's Ball"*

This scene in the show is a presentation of Hamilton's cockiness—especially when it came to the ladies. "A Winter's Ball" was written describing how Martha Washington named him after a feral tomcat (a rumor spread by John Adams), with punchy rhymes that barely skirt the tongue ("sister," "if, Burr").

## *"Helpless"*

Lin wrote a song he called, "This One's Mine" to mark the meeting of Alexander and Eliza in the show—but it didn't sound like the "final thing," as his wife Vanessa (his test audience) said. "Helpless" was his second attempt, beginning with establishing Eliza's personality—she was never the center of attention, unlike her sister Angelica, but with her older sibling's push, Alexander ended up meeting her and falling in love.

A turning point for Alexander's arrogance was right before his marriage to Eliza. The bridge of the song consists of him trying to give his new bride a dose of reality: that he was no one, he only had his "honor, a tolerance for pain, a couple of college credits and my top notch brain." These lines, with Miranda's unexpected growl rap in the last few lines, was an homage to hip hop duet master Ja Rule, and a repeated attempt to make actress Pippa Soo laugh.

# Chapter 9: One the Perfect Union of Actor and Role, with Allusion to Renée Elsie Goldsbrry

Angelica Schuyler's brain is as strong and fast and powerful as her personality—and Lin wrote the perfect song to match. The character shines in a solo track right after Hamilton marries her sister Eliza—right in the wedding reception, to be exact. "Satisfied" was filled to the hilt with fast bars and tongue-twisting lines, but it was never meant to be a song for showing off the actress' rapping and singing prowess. It was a representation of how the older Schuyler sister's thought process worked, and how that particular part of history is told differently in her eyes (which is why it literally rewinds back to the events in "Helpless," only it was focused on *her* feelings and views).

Renée Elsie Goldsberry almost didn't audition for the part—twice. She didn't relate to Miranda's description of the role (a mix of Nicki Minaj and Desiree Armfeldt), and she had a newly-adopted baby girl that took the top spot in her priority list. Still, the agents at Telsey+ Company sent her a demo of "Satisfied" and she was hooked, but she didn't have high hopes that she would get the part—she had one night to learn the lines.

But thanks to her Shakespeare performances and other rigorous roles under her belt, she was the first to depict how Angelica looked, sounded, and felt like—and she landed the character.

## "Satisfied"

Written by Miranda during his short stint in the NBC show *Do No Harm,* "Satisfied" was laid down the way Lin did his 8th grade personal literary essay: starting with the introduction (how Angelica met Alexander), statement of these (how she read Hamilton the minute she laid eyes on him), three proofs (the three fundamental truths she realized at the exact same time), and conclusion (her giving up her love in favor of her sister).

The song takes on a literal take on rewinding the events prior to the reception scene, retold in the eyes of the older Schuyler who didn't get the man. But in the end, Angelica steps aside for her sister, while the world chants, "be satisfied."

## "The Story of Tonight [Reprise]"

The show revisits "The Story of Tonight" after Hamilton marries—a checking in on what his friends thought of his new marital status, and a reaffirmation of their friendship and dedication to the revolution.

This also gives an update on the happenings and parallels between Alexander and his frenemy Aaron Burr. Alexander was promoted to Washington's Right Hand Man, Aaron became a Lieutenant Coronel with his own command. Hamilton married Eliza, Burr had a relationship with Theodosia (who was married to a British officer, no less). It was a testament to the fundamental difference in their temperament: Hamilton went for the whirlwind romance, Burr learned to wait for his opportunity to be with his woman.

# Chapter 10: The Same Subject Continued, with Allusion to Leslie Odom, Jr., Plus Remarks on the Virtues and Merits of Union

The success of *Hamilton* seemed inevitable, but it was anything but. The same goes for the actor who ended up landing the role of Aaron Burr, Hamilton's nemesis and the show's narrator.

In the summer of 2013, Lin, Tommy, Alex, and other collaborators took part in the series of developmental workshops at the New York Stage and Film in Poughkeepsie. After a week of isolated, concentrated work, the workshops yielded what would almost be the final version of Act One.

It was not without challenges, though. Usual musical formats have spoken lines in between songs—but it didn't work well with the hip hop and rap styles of *Hamilton*. There was no one else who can keep up with the show's progress to write alongside Lin—and so he took on penning the entirety of the scenes as songs.

When the group presented their work in front of an audience of 150, Leslie Odom, Jr. was among the people who stood up cheered on their feet. He sent a message of support to Lin— and Lin promptly expressed his desire for him to play Aaron Burr.

The actor who initially read the part was a little too similar to Lin, and Burr should be the complete opposite. Leslie seemed to have been tailor-fitted for the role—he was, in Miranda's words, "cool, his blood runs cool, he is elegant."

Leslie was not able to accept Lin's invitation to take part in the early workshops for Hamilton the first time due to his schedule—but on the second workshop, he came in, with Burr's part fully memorized.

He became so committed to the role that when faced with a choice between a TV role with NBC and *Hamilton,* Leslie didn't let go of Burr, calling it "arguably the best role for a male actor of color in the musical theater canon."

### *"Wait for It"*

Waiting and taking his time is Aaron Burr's go-to throughout the whole story—and "Wait for It" was the musical declaration of his code.

A dramatization of Burr's stasis, Lin, ironically enough, wrote the lines of the chorus loops while rushing to a friend's birthday party in Williamsburg, aboard the A train (a testimonial of how inspiration can strike literally anywhere at any time).

Lin's manner of lyricizing Aaron's inner thoughts gives the

audience a glimpse of his history and how it shaped his views, particularly on sitting back, and waiting for the right time (even the pregnant pauses before the "wait for it" line is meant to emphasize this).

# Chapter 11: Wherein Mob Deep is Sampled, and the Immortal Biggie Smalls is Revived

There were several elements in the *Hamilton* songs that pay homage to the greatest hip hop artists who also served as Lin's major influences in his own art form. In "My Shot," he sampled the opening siren effect in Mobb Deep's "Shook Ones, Pt. II," and injected its lyrics in one of the verses as well ("I'm only 19, but my mind is older").

Another notable tribute was the one Miranda gave the Notorious B.I.G., also known as Biggie Smalls, the greatest rapper of all time. "Ten Duel Commandments" took direction from his track, "Ten Crack Commandments," giving him the template of how to lay down the rules and code of dueling for when John Laurens and Charles Lee confronted each other—paving the way for when the inevitable Hamilton-Burr duel.

Sampling the sounds from these artists—and at times lifting lyrics out of the tracks themselves—goes beyond showing gratitude to the pioneers of the genre. Lin uses them as another way of telling the audience that this show is for a wider audience, and that history can be told and retold "by people who don't look like George Washington or Betsy Ross."

### *"Stay Alive"*

The song marks the period during the war where things looked bleak for the American forces. Hamilton raps about how their leader Washington had become despondent, how the soldiers had nothing to eat and were mostly refused help by the locals. They resorted to stealing supplies from the British and during this time, Hamilton still wants to lead and have his own command (Washington repeatedly rejects his requests). Lin takes the narrator role from Burr in this scene and passes it on to Alexander to portray the frustration, desperation, and his anger at not being able to perform at more active role n the war.

### *"Ten Duel Commandments"*

The Laurens-Lee duel sets the tone for how soldiers and men settled disputes during the 18th century. "Ten Duel Commandments" relies heavily on historian Joanne Freeman's book, *Affairs of Honor*. It also helped that she was one of the leading experts on the subject of Alexander Hamilton.

Again, Lin passes on the role of narrator—this time, to the company—not only to enumerate the ground rules for dueling, but also to establish that the practice was, indeed, a way of life back then, and not an unusual way to settle differences.

Hamilton and Burr act as seconds for Lee and Laurens, respectively—and shows how Burr is against dueling while Hamilton deems in necessary; it's a contrast to the fatal duel that they will find themselves in later on.

# Chapter 12: Of Oskar Eustis, His Politics, His Eventful Career, His Thoughts on Verse Drama, and His Stewardship of the Public Theater, with a Word About the Pharcyde

After the workshops in Poughkeepsie and the success of their presentation at Vassar, Lin and Tommy declared to their producer Jeffrey that they were ready to roll out the show before the end of 2014.

Seller was hesitant—the show didn't even have an Act Two at that point, and there was the question of where to showcase this innovative and groundbreaking show and ensuring maximum positive exposure. He suggested that they do a *Chorus Line*, and bring their unknown show to the Public Theater—it was the home of successful musical debuts, away from the pressures of Broadway.

Oskar Eustis, the artistic director for the Public, met Lin's demos and his visit to the theater with overwhelming enthusiasm. Along with executive director Patrick Willingham, they put in *Hamilton* for the 2014-2015 season—giving Lin one year to write the rest of the show and Tommy one year to figure out the execution.

Eustis' admiration for Miranda parallels his reverence to Shakespeare, no less. To him, the way Lin elevates the language of the people by turning it into verse is no different than how the poet interprets the foundational myths of history by ennobling the people and the language they use, making it everybody's possession.

Incidentally, Miranda did follow Shakespeare's genius directly—he revived the dead art of verse storytelling, as in *Medea, Tartuffe,* and *Othello,* by listening to "Friend or Foe" and "Everything is Fair" from Pharcyde's first album on a loop.

### *"Meet Me Inside"*

Washington telling off Hamilton's brash actions is told through this rare rap that starts with a 7/8 time signature. The chaos and mess of the bars matched the anger of the leader and the soldier's frustration—with the company egging him on using the menacing chant "Meet 'im inside" alluded from DMX's "Party It Up."

It eventually falls back to 4/4 as Washington tries to reason Hamilton yet again out of his desire to have a command of his own—he appeals to familiarity, calling him son several times, and it leads to an outburst that sends the soldier home. Lin notes that this scene with his friend Chris always varies every night—but stays as real and as emotional.

# Chapter 13: On Phillipa Soo and the Trouble with Goodness

After three unsuccessful tries on having Ron Chernow's book adapted as a Hollywood film, the author was enthusiastic about Lin giving Hamilton his due on the musical stage. The story had everything in it—violence, sex, and genius—but there was also a problematic element that needed to be addressed: Eliza Hamilton, and her pure, earnest goodness that needed to be made compelling enough as to not be overshadowed by, say, her fast-witted, strong headed sister Angelica.

But Tommy had found the solution while watching *Natasha, Pierre, and the Great Comet of 1812*—where he found the fresh Julliard graduate Phillipa Soo. She was invited to read for the role of Eliza during one of the workshops at the Public Theater on December 2013, and had been the only choice for the female lead ever since.

Pippa's innate elegance and warmth resonated Eliza's own, and it made the audience drawn to the otherwise more subdued Schuyler sister. The Chinese-American actress was able to navigate around the fast-paced changes surrounding her character's life throughout the play, thanks to conversations with Ron himself who regards his wife Valerie as Eliza's very personification—so much so that he put Hamilton's words about his wife on Valerie's gravestone when she died in 2006: "Best of Wives, and Best of Women."

## *"That Would Be Enough"*

Following Hamilton's forced leave from the war, "That Would Be Enough" is the song a very pregnant Eliza sings to Hamilton to ease his anxiety about being a poor soldier with seemingly no legacy. There was no historical references for this track—it was simply something that needed to be said between wife and husband, and Lin fast-tracked the first draft of the entire song in 45 minutes.

The last verse ("Oh let me be a part of the narrative, in the story they will write someday") is a marker for when Eliza wants Alexander to open up and share his own story with her—which will be revisited when Eliza ends her part of the 'narrative' as she learns of Hamilton's affair in "Burn."

# Chapter 14: On Paul Tazewell and the Fashion of Revolution

Paul Tazewell, even with his 20 years of experience in designing both contemporary and period costume for numerous other shows, faced the challenge of combining the modernity of hip hop and rap and the 18th century backdrop in *Hamilton*. But the concept was soon established: period fashion from the neck down, and present time diversity from the neck up. That meant no powdered wigs for the black and Latino actors—they could show themselves for who they are.

The costumes made their first appearance in the May 9, 2014 when Act One and Act Two of *Hamilton* was first previewed to an audience of 150 at the 52nd Street Project's top-floor theater. The audience cheered and wept by the end of the first half of the show, seeing soldiers of color wearing the uniforms of Washington's Continental Army, winning America's Freedom. The preview was presented in a period of four days, and by the end of the week, the total of 600 people who had first glimpse of the musical had already spread the news and made *Hamilton* the most talked-about (not quite finished) show in the city.

## "Guns and Ships"

Known for its rapid-fire bars and triplet rhythm rhymes, this song is a presentation of Marquis de Lafayette's character evolution throughout the war. Struggling with the pronunciation of 'anarchy' during his first few lines in "My Shot," he transforms into a rap demon who spits lyrics with expertise and speed while appealing Hamilton's case to George Washington. Lin hails Daveed Diggs, who took on the role of Lafayette, as one of the most technically gifted rappers that he knows and had no problem taking advantage of his lyrical dexterity for the track.

## "History Has Its Eyes on You"

In "History Has Its Eyes on You," Washington warns Hamilton of the results of recklessness—with an important historical tidbit from Washington's early days as commander, thanks to Ron Chernow's bio on the first President.

Washington's fame originated not from glory, but from shame—he led his men straight into a slaughter and helped ignite the French and Indian War, and the guilt of it remained with him until he died.

It also speaks of how no matter how history is on the hands of not those who lived it, but those who tells the story after those involved are long gone—something that applies to all the characters, and all of us. This gave way to Lin writing the line that would define the whole show: "Who Lives, Who Dies, Who Tells Your Story."

## *"Yorktown"*

The scene of the battle of Yorktown in 1781 starts of with Hamilton and Lafayette praising each other, smug about being the immigrants who get the job done. This establishes the rush of that final fight, and how Alexander finally realizes that his initial desire to die in glory in the war is now replaced with an urgency to end it and come home to his wife and son.

Taking inspiration from Busta Rhyme's soft-loud-soft style, the track speaks of removing bullets from guns and remaining quiet as to not get caught by the Brits—and then comes Mulligan, the spy on the inside, bursting with loud and proud lines on how he smuggled out information that would help his comrades win the war.

The song breaks into a 'fight scene,' one that the Americans win, and Lin injects the same drinking song that the British soldiers sang as they retreated the lines ("the world turned upside down")—a fitting way to present the sentiment of their victory.

# Chapter 15: By Which It will Appear that Good History Makes Good Drama, and in Which Sebastian Miranda Makes His Debut

.The victory in Yorktown could have been a dramatic, high ending for Act One, but Lin surmised that it was missing something. Founding Father John Adams refused to see that winning the battle was a painless birth of a new nation, and ending the first half with the triumph blinded the audience of the mess that followed a newborn country at the end of a long war.

So they extended it with songs that foreshadowed the difficulties and conflicts that lie ahead. It starts with a petulant King George, a sore loser that warns the Americans of the hardships of ruling—and his smug prediction that they will come crawling back to Britain the minute they realize how challenging it is to be on their own. The delivery was comical, but the message sobering.

A monumental moment in Hamilton's personal life was also happening during this time—his son Philip was born in 1782. And because he amazingly parallels Burr, his daughter Theodosia was born shortly after in 1783. The duet "Dear Theodosia" was an I-promise song from the fathers to the younger generation, something that resonated deeply within

Lin himself—but because he adopted his dog during the time he wrote it. The performances, however, wells from another parenting legacy: the birth of his son Sebastian.

Hamilton, however, was not exactly the model husband or father, and it worried Lin that it would alienate the audience from the deeply-flawed character.

His alternate, Javier Muñoz, doesn't agree—it's the flaws that drew him to the role, and even with just doing the show once every week, he knew the audience responded to the role as he did.

### *"What Comes Next?"*

King George pops in the scene right after the victorious rush of "Yorktown," all glum and bitter—but also with a dose of reality for the winners. He asks the important question— what will they do with their freedom and their new country? Ruling was a thankless, lonely job.

It prepares the audience for audience for the political themes of the second act: they win the war in Act One, they govern in the next.

### *"Dear Theodosia"*

Lin wrote "Dear Theodosia" during what he called the calm of the storm of his life. It was 2011, and he and his wife

Vanessa were on vacation in the Dominican Republic—but the trip was a somber one, due to his aunt-in-law Isolde's struggles during the final stages of ALS.

This was when a stray puppy came to them on the beach, began nipping on their ankles begging to be adopted (they named it Tobillio, Spanish for 'ankle'). Vanessa's aunt died, they adopted the dog, and found Tobillo's sister a family—it was both a sad and happy moment for the family, and the emotions translated into the duet for Hamilton and Burr.

It spoke of the uncertainties the new fathers felt, but promising a better nation for the younger generation. Having grown up without fathers, both promise to be around for their children.

### *"Tomorrow There'll Be More of Us"*

This song is another revisiting of "The Story of Tonight," marking the death of Alexander's close friend John Laurens. This particular part of the play was not included in the cast album, mainly because Lin sees it as more of a scene than a standalone track. It comes swiftly after the joy of declaring his fatherly promises to his son—through a letter from Laurens' father telling him of his demise.

As the most prolific militant against slavery, he was also more reckless and passionate than Hamilton and Lafayette, and his death is what Lin calls the biggest what-if in history: if he hadn't died, what work would he have done to emancipate the slaves? He was a war veteran, a friend to influential individuals who rose to fame and glory during the war, and a favorite of the commander Washington himself. What would have been his impact on the freeing of the slaves will forever be unknown.

Hamilton was a verbose, opinionated man—and there are countless documents in his own writing and in others' to prove it. But there was little to be read about how he grieved for his dear friend—and it says something about how he processed loss—and the death of someone who was precious to him (some surmise that they had been lovers at one point).

# Chapter 16: On "Non-Stop," Both the Song and the Way of Life, as Manifest by Andy Blankenbuehler and the Public Theater's Props Department

On January, merely eight days before they present *Hamilton* for the first time at the 290-seater Newman Theater at the Public, tech rehearsals and props refinement were at their crunch time—and with 1,300 cues to perfect, they were cutting it close.

Jay Duckworth and his colleagues at the props department took care of every single minute detail—from the replica of Rochambeau's map for Washington's scene to the pamphlets that were scribbled with Latin gibberish so they wouldn't distract the audience should they catch them, the tiniest things (down to a personalized wax seal for each character) didn't escape their eyes. When asked why he give this much attention to what would be least seen in the play, he takes his time and simply utters, "'Cause it *has* to be." This attention to detail channels Hamilton's own; he fussed and worried over the smallest things, from organizing the US army, to designing the uniforms and choosing the color for Washington's plume and buttons.

And when it came to the details of the choreography, Andy

Blankenbuehler was, as Miranda tweeted, a relentless genius. In "Non-Stop," six years' worth of Hamilton's life is crammed into 12 scenes of fast-paced events in the span of 6 minutes, and Andy matched the "venom" and vitality of it with dance.

He first worked with Lin in *In the Heights*—a salsa and hip-hop laden musical where he confessed to knowing little about. But Lin saw him as a great storyteller and hired him anyway—and it got him a Tony Award.

Devising "stylized heightened gestures," Andy created custom moves for every single character (Burr moves in uncompromising straight lines, Hamilton in messy arches), down to the way the props are held—things that aren't always noticeable to the audience. But this microscopic focus on a macroscopic scale created the choreography that matches what the scene wants the audience to feel.

Which brings the center of the stage to the point: the two spinning turntables. Korin's idea was initially set aside, but when they revisited the concept days before the opening night, Andy supported the idea—and the cast had to relearn the dances with the two moving platforms included. The chaos seemed to reflect Andy's own life: while he worked on *Hamilton,* his daughter was undergoing chemotherapy, and he moved his family around a lot to adjust to the rigors of both working and living each day to the fullest with his kids.

The indispensability of not just Lin, but every single collaborator and members of the group comprising the *Hamilton* musical parallels the importance of not just Hamilton himself, but of all the founding fathers and key individuals during the first years of America as a free country.

## *"Non-Stop"*

The song begs the question: what makes a relentless genius? "Non-stop" is a quick rundown of Hamilton's life from when he returned from the war in 1783, to becoming a member of the cabinet in 1789. A "colonial clusterfuck," as Lin calls it, this song ends Act One with a flurry of multilayered melodies, spinning sets, and massive motion from the company and leads.

It starts with re-establishing how Hamilton and Burr seem to go through life in uncannily similar ways: they become lawyers almost at the same time, and practice in the same city. But the likenesses doesn't take away from their stark differences—Alexander was still hotheaded and passionate, Burr calm and biding his time.

Hamilton's obsessive writing is mentioned in this song ("why do you write like you're running out of time?"), his controversial idea of a pseudo-king leader for America that he proposed during his six-hour speech at the constitutional convention, and his idea of writing the Federalist Papers, which he encouraged Burr to join.

Burr, the non-risk taker, refuses to help—an emphasis on them being fundamental opposites.

Meanwhile, Angelica sails off to London with her new husband, and Eliza is dismayed at her husband's lack of satisfaction with the simple life. Still, Alexander persists and goes on to write the Papers and becomes a member of Washington's cabinet as the Treasury Secretary.

# ACT II

## Chapter 17: In New York You Can Be a New Man, or, the Story of Oak and Daveed

Act Two opens with two Virginian would-be presidents of the United States—and Hamilton's nemeses—Thomas Jefferson and James Madison.

Lin and Tommy agreed on the irony that the actors who played Alexander's closest friends (Lafayette and Mulligan) would also play his greatest foes in the second half—and they needed artists who could convincingly and compellingly do both. Lafayette the freedom fighter who raps multiple bars in one breathe would become the French-loving, jazz-singing, laidback Jefferson, and the brash, loud, and proud Mulligan would turn into the well-born, shy and sickly Madison.

Daveed Diggs and Okieriete Onaodowan took over those transformations, respectively. For Daveed, who performed with the Freestyle Love Supreme with Lin and lead his own avante-garde hip hop group Clipping, the duality of bursting rapid-fire, highly technical raps on the first half of the show and then belting out jazz tunes came as naturally to him, being the half-black, half-Jewish kid from the tough parts of Oakland who went to Brown.

Oak, on the other hand, did more than a personality switch in the show: the towering, 235-pound actor had to 'shrink' himself from the growling, revolutionary who took up space with his huge movements to the coughing, nasal politician who meekly trailed behind his partner Jefferson. He took over the roles with relish—he was sick of doing shows "about a messed-up black kid."

Seeing black men slip into the roles of Jefferson, Washington, and Madison as a kid could have been, in Daveed's eyes, a life-changing experience. And for Oak, who grew up poor in West Orange, New Jersey, discouraged by mentors early on, the role of Madison was a godsend. The acclaim and feelings of accomplishment sank in as the crowd grew in the lobby of the Public Theater, waiting to shake their hands and take selfies with the actors who revolutionized musicals.

### *"What'd I Miss?"*

Thomas Jefferson's return to New York is marked by a jazzy, proto-hip hop tune (a cocktail of Lambert, Hendricks, Ross, Gil Scott-Heron), emphasizing that the older politician, for the most part of the War, was absent while the rest of the country moved on to hip hop and rap. Andy and Tommy staged his arrival with Jefferson coming down the stairs, servants cleaning and wiping the floor and carrying his luggage: a picture of the irony that the person who articulated liberty so passionately and clearly was, in fact, an owner of several slaves.

Madison's fallout with Hamilton after writing the Federalist Papers was left to the audience' imagination in the intermission, and the song establishes him seeking the charismatic Thomas to help him oppose Hamilton's financial plan.

# Chapter 18: An Account of Rapping for the Children, Who Will One Day Rap for Themselves

*Hamilton the Musical*, was a smash hit—the rave reviews and overwhelming response by viewers sold out tickets faster than anyone expected. And a few weeks after opening night, they opened their doors to teenagers from New York City public schools through the Theater Development Fund. Lin was nervous because, as he tweeted, "Like Shakira's hips, kids don't lie."

The lasting impact of the show on the students was, as Ginger Bartkoski Meagher of TDF says, *transformative*. The follow up programs allowed the participants to talk about what societal issues they felt were important to them—such as gun control, and same-sex marriage—in rap battle, like in the Cabinet Meetings in *Hamilton*. Discussions about the play and how it connects to history and the now were also enthusiastically partaken. The program was such a success that the Rockefeller Foundation put out a whopping $1.5 million grant to allow 20,000 more public school students in New York to see the musical and participate in the Gilder Lehrman Institute of American History educational program—for just $10.

Soon, the show will be open for licensing to school and

amateur productions—and given its appealing genre and impactful subject matter, it is predicted to be one of the most licensed musicals in the country. The way *Hamilton* was crafted and executed—bringing in the language of the common people and welcoming color in an otherwise predominantly white show—will, as Lin hopes, be reflected in the future productions and have the same message of diversity.

## *"Cabinet Battle #1"*

The first rap battle in the show—presided by the Mekhi Phiper in *Hamilton*, President Washington—was all about interpreting the debates (the stakes of which include the direction the entire country takes and the enormous national debt) in a contemporary language. Jefferson declares it unfair for those who create (the southerners) to bail the rest of the country, thanks to Hamilton who just wants to move money around—Alexander points out that all the money they had came from not paying the slaves in their fields.

Hamilton, Like Lin, runs cold when provoked into anger—he spits fire and goes into a verbose attack. But Thomas was a worthy opponent, and Washington splits up the two with a recess, but not without a final jab from Jefferson referencing Grandmaster Flash ("such a blunder sometimes it makes me wonder why I even bring the thunder").

# Chapter19: Did They or Didn't They? Or, Some Discourse on Affairs

Hamilton gets entangled in two extramarital affairs in the show: one is a regret-filled, sex-driven series of trysts with the married Maria Reynolds, the other a less obvious, but tension-filled push-and-pull with none other than his sister-in-law Angelica.

Lin, to Chernow's delight, respected the ambiguity of Alexander's relationship with the older Schuyler sister. He took some poetic liberties, changing the timeline so that Hamilton met Angelica before Eliza, sparking the undeniable chemistry between the two, and continuing the flirtation through letter when she moved to London with her husband.

Angelica was more than the woman who had the "emotional affair" with Hamilton—she also was his greatest political confidant, pouring her intelligence and strong opinions through her letters—because there was nowhere else to do it, being a woman during those times. They are two peas in a pod and seem to perfectly match each other's wit and passions—but Lin firmly believes that Eliza is still the right Schuyler for Alexander, a sentiment that Renèe agrees on. Eliza was the constant source of goodness and warmth and wisdom—something that Alexander severely needed.

## *"Take a Break"*

"Take a Break" shows this dynamic between the husband, the wife, son, and sister-in-law while zipping through at least seven plot points all within a four-and-a-half-minute marker.

During the workshops, Lin was told by a respected musical composer that the song was good, but unnecessary. He took it on as a challenge to prove that the track deserved to be in the final cut—it was an important check-in on Hamilton's personal and family situation, and reestablishes Angelica's important in his life amidst all the politically-driven songs and themes.

Playing with *Macbeth* lines and characters in a verse, Hamilton writes one of his flirtatious letters to his sister-in-law, before getting to hear his son Philip do a simple and childish rap—with his mother on beatbox.

It also presents Angelica as Alexander's advisor—she urges him to do whatever it takes to convince Jefferson of what he wanted to do and get the congress votes. Then the written are-they-aren't-they interaction continues ("you've written 'my dearest, Angelica'") before telling him to meet her when she visits the family upstate. Of course, even with Eliza's pleading and Angelica's prodding, he chooses to stay and work on his financial plan.

# Chapter 20: In Which Advantages are Derived from Listening to the Broadway Old Masters and Jasmine Cephas Jones

Lin-Manuel grew up listening to countless cast albums—his very DNA is embedded with show tunes and songs of Broadway musicals. As he developed *Hamilton*, he delved deeper and got inspiration and advice from the best mentors in the industry.

*Cabaret* and *Chicago* composer John Kander met Lin when he saw *In the Heights* in 2007, and when the American Songbook concert and workshops came, he was invited to witness the first stages of the Hamilton project. Kander's diligence towards work and tireless drive to create inspired Lin to keep going—he learned from him that a writer can live a happy, contended life, and still be able to pull the necessary darkness and pain and chaos to make compelling material.

Master Broadway librettist John Weidman also played a huge part in helping Lin plow through the historical heaviness of *Hamilton*. Miranda was swimming in research—and he sought Weidman's wisdom on where his creativity can squeeze through without getting too overwhelmed with the pressures of historical accuracy. He provided a lot of assurance—that it was both provocative and significant to tell America's history and how it is similar to America today.

In 2008, Lin was hired to do translations for the Puerto Rican production of *West Side Story*—and met the legend behind other musicals such as *Sweeney Todd* and *Sunday in the Park with George:* Stephen Sondheim.

Sondheim was all aboard with Lin's revolutionary reinvention of musicals—he, in fact, also used rap to tell the backstory of the witch during the opening number of *Into the Woods*. He did, however, know that rap and hip hop can create monotony if not balanced properly.

He knew that Lin took his advice in mind with "Say No to This," the hip-hop / R&B song where the Hamilton-Reynolds affair is established in the show—the track that actress Jasmine Cephas Jones calls "her jam."

Growing up in a performing family (her father is actor Ron Cephas Jones, and her mother Kim Lesley is a jazz singer), the Berklee graduate valued the opportunity of taking on a role of a musical theater character with a non-traditional style of singing. She was able to sing without copping a style that isn't her own, and as a person of color, got to play the role of a white woman without having to change herself.

Like Oak's and Daveed's, Jasmine's parts in the show also

called for duality—the vivacious daddy's girl Peggy Schuyler (the youngest of the three sisters), and the seductive, sultry Maria Reynolds, wife of an abusive husband and Hamilton's provocative mistress.

### *"Say No to This"*

There is yet another shift in the narrators as Burr sets the scene ("there's nothing like summer in the city"), and quickly passes on to Alexander—the only one who could tell the story of the affair as accurately as he experienced it.

It zigzags between Hamilton's rap bars, Maria's soulful R&B hooks, James Reynold's hip hop verses, and back into Hamilton and Maria's combined, anguished confrontation—with the company chanting, "No!" in the background. Hamilton was trapped—if he didn't pay off Reynolds, Eliza would find out about the affair. Maria plead her case as well—she was helpless, and more than willing to continue their relationship should he agree to bribe the husband.

In the end, he gives in to the blackmail, ending with, "nobody needs to know," a nod to the song by Jason Robert Brown for *The Last Five Years*.

# Chapter 21: On Being in "The Room Where it Happens" with the Cast of *A Chorus Line*—Plus a Brief Account of Nevin Steinberg Bringing Boom-Bap to Broadway with Speakers the Size of Refrigerators

As a tribute to the 40th anniversary of *A Chorus Line*, the legendary musical about the struggles of Broadway dancers, The *Hamilton* cast lined up spanning the entire stage, holding their headshots against their faces, the very same way the cast of the revered show did four decades earlier.

The story of *A Chorus Line* rings true to most stage performers—the *Hamilton* ensemble included. The impactful movements that bring the show alive, thanks to Andy's exhaustive, dynamic choreography, would not be possible without the men and women who tirelessly sing and dance, embodying those that they represent—the people who fought for the freedom of their country, and built it from the ashes of the war.

The "ensemble of soloists," as Andy called them, comprised of five males and four females as part of the original cast at the Public Theater: Carleigh Bettiol, the lovely maiden sashaying across the "Winter's Ball," Ariana De Bose, the "bullet" who traced its dangerous path towards Hamilton,

Jon Rua and Thayne Jasperson, whose exuberant moves livened the stage in an effort to catch Angelica's attention in "Schuyler Sisters" and portray the passionate fervor of the revolution in "My Shot," respectively, Sydney James Harcourt, who, at one point, shushed the garrulous Hamilton as Philip Schuyler in "Helpless," Sasha Hutchings who floated lifelessly in the air, representing Alexander's dead mother, Seth Stewart and Ephraim Sykes, who spun, twirled, slid, and fired muskets with precise and powerful grace, and Betsy Struxness, the veteran Broadway performer with the most credits under her name, zigzagging through the stage looking like three different blonde dancers all at once.

When the *Hamilton* cast sang "What I Did for Love" in their tribute, the ensemble took over the lead singing—and the 19 cast members of *A Chorus Line* joined them onstage, met by a long and loud standing ovation.

That day almost did not come to fruition—most expected that *Hamilton* would cancel its extended run in the Public Theater so it can make its debut in Broadway before the Tony Awards deadline in April and have better chances of winning best musical. But as Oskar Eustis announced atop a bar counter in the Public on a press conference, the show completed its extensions and set to reopen at the Richard Rogers Theater in July 2015.

It was the same sentiment that Michael Bennet had with *A Chorus Line*—they wanted to take the time to fine-tune *Hamilton* before its Broadway debut—five months, to be exact.

The show underwent several tweaks and adjustments: Andy refined the choreography, Paul Tazewell reevaluated and altered costumes, and Nevin Steinberg worked on seamlessly incorporating audio equipment to better balance the sounds that Alex and the band played.

Nevin decided to put to use his two large, refrigerator-sized subwoofers (designed for stadiums, not theaters) inconspicuously on either side of the proscenium arch of the Richard Rogers Theater during tech rehearsals, and as Lin walked in, the band started the banjo-injected, straight-ahead boom-bap hip hop song "The Room Where It Happens." It was enough for Miranda to yell, "Oh fuck *everybody!*"

## *"The Room Where it Happens"*

Legacy is something that the men of the 18th century worked and toiled for—and Hamilton and Burr, war veterans and lawyers, were no different. "The Room Where it Happens" starts off with the two bitterly gossiping about Clermont Street renamed after the general who died in battle—while the two are still alive and triumphant with no roads under their names.

Then they start talking politics—and this is where the break starts to crack for Burr. Hamilton was still on the losing side with his financial plan, but as he mentions ("I guess I'm finally gonna have to listen to you (Burr)"), he's starting to act the way Aaron does to leverage his way and get what he wants from Madison and Jefferson—in a dinner that Burr wasn't invited to.

This is where he realizes that he was being overtaken by Alexander using *his* way of doing things—so why wasn't he in the room where it happens? Burr sings and dances at the unfairness of it all. The tension heightens, the ensemble eggs Burr on, asking: "What do you want, Burr?"

He was just as intelligent, just as qualified—and he knows the art of the compromise more than the stubborn loud Hamilton—of course he knew what he wanted: to be in the Room Where It Happens.

### *"Schuyler Defeated"*

This short track marks the beginning of Burr actively seeking out power. He unseats the Schuyler patriarch and takes his post as New York senator, and Hamilton confronts him—and Burr pointedly tells him that the people don't trust Alexander, and that he just seized the opportunity that he saw. It ends with a warning, "I swear your pride will be the death of us all! Beware: it goeth before the fall..."

## *"Cabinet Battle #2"*

The second rap battle in the show is still between Hamilton and Jefferson—this time, about the issue of whether the United States will provide aid to the French who started to rebel as well against England.

This is where Jefferson really gets into his conflict with the Treasury Secretary. As Secretary of State, he insists that Hamilton's position has no bearing on deciding state affairs—something that *he* was in charge of. And as former French ambassador, he maintains that America owes France a debt and a promise to aid them as the latter supported the former when they fought against the British forces. He ends his tirade with the famous line from Notorious B.I.G.'s "Juicy" ("And if ya don't know, now ya know").

Hamilton, of course, does not take this sitting down. He cites the young country's fragile economic situation and the perils of non-stop war-waging—something that, to Jefferson's dismay, Washington agrees to. Alexander wins the rap battle. The song closes with Jefferson taking a jab at Hamilton being the president's pet.

# Chapter 22: A Picture of the Recording Studio, Featuring Learned Comments by Questlove and a Thrown Shoe

Questlove, the hip hop living legend who plays drums for the Roots, leads the house band in the Jimmy Fallon show, and author of *Mo'Meta Blues* (a musical guru, all in all), was not a stranger to attempts at bringing hip hop to Broadway. They all seemed disappointingly similar—all spray cans and the Bronx and breakdances—until he saw *Hamilton*. He was so impressed by the production that he wondered, "Is this the most revolutionary thing to happen to Broadway, or the most revolutionary thing to happen to hip hop?"

He felt that the show embodies the tricks that the 40-something-year-old genre still had up in its sleeves—and only someone like Lin, who took a history bio on vacation, could do it.

And Lin's intentions for hip-hop *are* revolutionary—he wanted to inject it to Broadway's DNA, the same way *Hair* and *Rent* did with rock—and the results gained the respect and admiration of a long list of the genre's legendary artists and producers: Busta Rhymes, Q-Tip, Common, Queen Latifah, Talib Kweli, Missy Elliot, Hammer, Chance the Rapper, Jay Z, RZA, DJ Premiere Salaam Remi, Pharell

Willams). It even landed Lin, Daveed, and Renèe a cypher bit in the BET Awards with Questlove and Black Thought (The Roots' lead MC). Questlove likens *Hamilton's* power of unifying such different demographic together to Michael Jackson's "Thriller."

He and Black Thought ended up becoming the executive producers to the *Hamilton* cast album, recorded at the Avatar Records in Midtown. This is where the performers got to really appreciate the intricacies of Lin's scores and Lacamoire's (or Lac, as they call him) orchestrations. Questlove saluted the musical director's work as well, reveling at how Lac was so self-assured about the sound he wants and his drive to get it.

It also highlighted and magnified the cast's vocal prowess, so much so that when Leslie came up to record "Wait for It" in front of him, Tommy, Lac, and producer Bill Sherman, someone threw a shoe against the recording booth's window in a display of violent enthusiasm.

The cast album charted higher than any Broadway album since *Camelot* (500+ years ago), and went on to receive four and a half stars from *Rolling Stones,* and a full five-star review *and* "Best Hip Hop Album of 2015" from *Billboard.* It not only legitimized the show in the hip hop scene—it also

73

changed the way people viewed hip hop and what it can do—the stories it could tell.

## *"Washington on Your Side"*

Questlove calls "Washington on Your Side" a "tug of war" song, where Jefferson, Madison, and Burr spit rap lines and finish each other's sentences in a fast-paced back and forth, starting from dissing Hamilton to plotting and scheming to formulate the plan to destroy him—all with a rare swing beat in the background.

From affronting Alexander's fashion choices, to being Washington's favorite, to breaking down the injustice of his financial plans, the lyrics became a cascade of ideas that led to one goal: getting rid of Hamilton. The polysyllabic, Kendrick Lamar-style of Jefferson's rapping about his resignation was a quick transition from his jazz singing from when he first appeared.

# Chapter 23: On the Origin and Persistence of Our National Shame

After the show closed at the Public, the team took a few weeks off and returned for rehearsals at the New 42nd Street Studios.

In one room, it was a period of reinventing the choreography for Andy—they added two swings to the original three so they can substitute right away in cases of illness or emergencies, and Alysha Deslorieux stood on standby to be a Schuyler sister or Maria Reynolds. He reworked the moves for the roof-shaking final chorus of "The Room Where It Happens."

Next door, Tommy rehearsed with the main actors. He ran through the scenes with each individual, asking them to "open the bag up," or redo the same lines in different ways— it was a process of seeing new discoveries, new mistakes.

One of the bigger changes made in the show was with "One Last Ride," the song for Washington's stepping-down scene. The version done at the Public was a concentration of events (Hamilton drafting the Farewell Address, to the Whiskey Rebellion, to the speech itself)—and under Oskar's advice, Lin and Tommy reworked the track into a simpler one depicting only what serves the Story. It added how

Washington's resignation affected Alexander, and how Washington's favorite "fig and tree" verse from the Scripture fit so perfectly with his retirement—he wanted so badly to return to Mt. Vernon.

The song's second meaning—that all men and women should be able to find safe haven in America—rung too true to the heart when a white supremacist gunned down one of the oldest black churches in the US, the Emanuel A.M.E. Church in Charleston, North Carolina.

For Chris Jackson, who plays the first President, the founding fathers not eradicating slavery when the Union was formed was one of their biggest failures—and it is still plaguing the nation to this day. He was never able to reconcile that the role he plays was of a man who owned people, but he owns the character and considers having three black presidents in the show their "own form of protest."

### *"One Last Time"*

A rewrite of the Public Theater version of "One Last Ride," this song presents the time when Washington asked Hamilton to write his resignation speech—to the latter's utter surprise and dismay.

Lin took out passages from the actual Farewell Address,

76

which aims to paint the founding father as a human who commits mistakes. This couplet from "The Benign Influence of Good Laws Under a Free Movement" not only moves the heart but also reflects Hamilton's own sentiments.

Hamilton proceeds to write the Address, using spoken word as Washington layers in and sings the same lines, with the same music of "The Story of Tonight," reappearing after Laurens death—a nostalgic addition to the scene. The ensemble then chants a variation of the lines from Jefferson's arrival, "George Washington's coming home," while Hamilton asks him to "teach 'em how to say goodbye," an emphasis on Washington stepping down from presidency—a model for the future leaders to follow.

# Chapter 24: Oh Jonathan Groff, His Royal Character, His Notable Career, His Dressing Room Décor &C.

King George the Third's character appears in but a total of nine minutes throughout the whole show, but his distinct presence is just as memorable—and the sociopathic, Beatle-esque crooning was the perfect Broadway comeback for Jonathan Groff.

After making his successful debut onstage in *Spring Awakening*, Groff ventured into television, with his recurring role in *Glee* and the HBO drama *Looking*. He even dabbled on dubbing the voice of Kristoff in the Disney hit *Frozen*. His career trajectory was right on track, and yet he still chose to spend the following season doing what was essentially a cameo, dressed in extremely heavy robes.

Being a part of something as revolutionary as *Hamilton* made it easy for him to relinquish his small screen endeavors. The show, as he quotes, "comes along once in a generation." So eight times per week, he struts to the middle of the stage on his cues, the comical, mad, perplexed royalty who sings a love song laced with psychopathic tendencies. After which, he settles back into his nest, the dressing room he shares with Lin, where his door is replaced with his beaded curtain.

## *"I Know Him"*

The reappearance of King George was inspired by what the actual historical figure said upon hearing of Washington's resignation ("If he does that, he will be the greatest man in the world."). The first president was stepping down, to be replaced by the "little guy" John Adams—something that the British ruler "wasn't aware that was something a person could do."

The perplexed king cheers merrily at the impeding political chaos, bidding the second American leader good luck.

# Chapter 25: On Killing Your Darlings, with Reference to "Adams Administration," the Seductions of Benjamin Franklin, and Songs on the Cutting-Room Floor

The off-Broadway version of *Hamilton* was far longer than what made it to the Richard Rogers Theater—but even then, reviews often cited that Lin could trim down the running time. He responded as he received the Best Musical award from the New York Drama Critics Circle, "I'm not going to cut 15 minutes."

That does not mean all of Lin's songs made the cut. A drunken track with Hamilton, Laurens, Lafayette, and Mulligan about Alexander's sexual conquests was replaced by the less NSFW "A Winter's Ball." The demo of "Valley Forge," a gruesome account of the carnage in the Revolutionary War, had but a few surviving lines in "Stay Alive." Banjamin Franklin's country-rock songs were eliminated, as with the character. Eliza's "Let It Go," where she tries to hold Hamilton back from is anger towards Burr and his campaigns against her father for the senate seat was set aside, just as the scenes for it were.

The seemingly endless flow of ideas and testing those ideas between Lin and his collaborators reflected Hamilton's own non-stop genius, but it had something vital that their main character did not: self-restraint. They were able to make the necessary do-aways while keeping the overarching picture in mind.

### *"The Adams Administration [Full Lyrics]"*

Hamilton absolutely despised John Adams, and "The Adams Administration" displays in in its full, cussing relentlessness. The song initially included passages from Alexander's 54-page scathing pamphlet criticizing Adams, but lengthening the song, as funny as it would be to show Hamilton sputtering in rage, did not make sense since Adams was a non-present character in the show.

Hamilton's unhinged actions—concentrated down to cursing John Adams and throwing a thick tome of papers from the balcony—has his three rivals—Jefferson, Burr, and Madison—reconvening and cementing their plans to get rid of him.

# Chapter 26: In Which the Hero Blows Up His Spot, with the Assistance of Howard Binkley's Lights and Other Formats of Ingenuous Stagecraft

Hamilton, like the Founding Fathers, built the nation one paragraph at a time—it was a writer's revolution. But as monumentally uplifting as words may be, they can also cause utter despair and downfall—and Alexander's loquacious hand did more damage to himself than his political enemies.

The next four songs in the second Act portray this—his three nemeses knew about the checks he disbursed, and Alexander chose to expose his sex scandal through a pamphlet: a preemptive strike against whatever they were planning to ruin his reputation. It was dramatic, yes, but how can one represent the chaos and explosion of such events onstage?

"Hurricane" retraces Hamilton's childhood and the disasters than befell him—and taking cues from *The Wiz* items and people from his past start whirling around him, with Howard Binkley's ingenuous lighting giving off a purplish, eery, dreamlike effect.

In the "Reynold's Pamphlet," Hamilton's decision to write what would ruin him and hsis marriage needed to look like a bomb detonating—hence, the "sledgehammer effect" of the bright white flares on the opening note, and Nevin's monstrous sound system shaking the theater floor while dancers erupted.

Then, the silence. The aftermath of what Alexander had done shifts to Eliza, bathed in moonlight, otherwise cloaked in darkness as she erases herself from the narrative, burning her husband's love letters.

## "We Know"

This scene where Burr, Jefferson, and Madison confronts Hamilton with his suspected corruption starts with the three finishing off each other's lines and digging at Hamilton's Caribbean roots with Jamaican jargon ("Ya best g'wan run back where ya came from"), before Alexander starts what would be his self-imposed ruin: he shares the letters from James Reynolds, and the bribes he had issued with his own money (the song reverts back to "Say No To This" as Jefferson reads the letter).

## "Hurricane"

As Hamilton is faced by the possibility of his three enemies using what they know against him, his whole life flashes back down to when the hurricane destroyed his home when he was a child and his mother's death. "Hurricane" is tasked to condense Alexander's life and its tragedies and triumphs—and how he survived by the sheer power of his writing.

He wrote his way out of poverty, the island, the revolution, until he rose in his ranks, until Eliza fell in love with him. He concludes that writing will save him from *this* predicament—he will write the Reynold's Pamphlet.

In the last few verses, Burr sings his theme ("wait for it, wait for it"), anticipating Hamilton's self-destruction.

### *"The Reynolds Pamphlet"*

It was the nation's first sex scandal—and the song is just as crazy and frenzied. Lin used the beat from one of the songs that didn't make the final set list ("No John Trumbull"), and actual lines from the real "Reynolds Pamphlet" (updating the language for easier audience listening).

As Jefferson, Madison, and Burr start jeering Alexander ("Well, he's never gon' be president now"), Angelica comes sweeping in ("All the way from London—damn!") and throws back some lines from "Satisfied," clearly regretting matchmaking her sister with him. This was a cut from "Congratulations," another song on the cutting room floor, meant to be squeezed in between "The Reynolds Pamphlet" and "Burn," but was added to the former to heighten the sense of Alexander's world crushing down: his enemies are celebrating, he exposed his own affairs, and even his confidant Angelica now despises him. Everyone prances around a stricken Hamilton, and even King George sashays in to join the fun.

## *"Burn"*

Eliza Hamilton *did* burn letters—her husband's and whatever reactions she may have had following the exposure of Alexander's scandal. This gave Lin a huge creative leeway and steered the story towards her reaction being erasing *her* reaction from memory.

Lin injects Eliza's theme—this time, instead of wanting to be a part of the narrative (as in "That Would Be Enough"), she's erasing herself from it. Miranda actually developed this theme with "Burn," and went back to the earlier song to rewrite the 'narrative' elements in it. Some quotes from Angelica's letters to her distraught sister (found by Chernow) are also included ("you have married an Icarus; he has flown too close to the sun").

# Chapter 27: Giving an Account of a Hurricane, with a Notable Appearance by President Obama, and the Remarkable Rise of Anthony Ramos

The reception that *Hamilton* received was nothing short of a phenomenon—even more so for Anthony Ramos, the John Laurens and Philip Hamilton of the original cast. As he told his teary-eyed cast mates during their company meeting the day after opening, "I don't know about y'all, but it's been a long road to get here. A long road."

The youngest actor in the team came from the touch parts of Brooklyn, and earned a scholarship to enter the American Musical and Dramatic Academy. He landed small roles here and there after, and was actually declined for *In the Heights* three years before he tried out for *Hamilton.*

Lin's lyrics hit home to Anthony. Where he came from, some really didn't make it past 20. He learned to fight for what he stood up for, but he wasn't someone who wants to fight at all—something that he shares with his characters.

On July 18th, 2015, President Obama himself came to watch the show, and after taking photographs with the stunned cast during intermission and greeting Lin (who wasn't playing that night; it was Javier Muñoz' day to perform) and his parents, he turned one last time before heading back to the audience for Act Two and told Anthony: "You're really gifted."

### *"Blow Us All Away"*

Originally called, "Ya Boy is Killin' Em," this song reintroduces the nineteen-year-old Philip Hamilton (after his rapping cameo in "Take a Break")—and establishes his cocky, intelligent debonair character, with the females swooning all over him a al "Shoop" from Salt-N-Pepa.

He confronts George Ecker, one of his father's critics, and ends up challenging him to a duel. He, of course, knows nothing about dueling, and asks his father for advice. Hamilton tells him to fire a shot in the air to appease the other and end the fight—an actual practice called "delope." But Ecker fires before the counting is finished, and Philip gets shot.

### *"Stay Alive [Reprise]"*

Philip's body is pulled away as the scene shifts to the doctor's. Hamilton bursts in, fearful of what had happen and not knowing how his son was doing. Eliza soon follows, erupting into hysterics as the ensemble sings the same lines as she did for her husband during the war ("Stay alive").

Philip goes back into a heart wrenching banter with his mother about changing the notes when they played piano, and he takes his last breath.

# Chapter 28: A Grieving Chapter: On Losses Beyond Words

*Hamilton* was full of questions that mark the limits of what each character, who are distinctively intelligent, can comprehend ("What'd I miss?" Jefferson asks. "What is it like in his shoes?" Burr wonders. "Would that be enough?" Eliza wants to know).

It was Lin's big challenge. How does he save Hamilton's marriage when Eliza wants him to burn? And at that point of the show, how does he show the grief of losing Philip when he himself has never experienced such loss?

Not being able to understand *was* the answer. Lin wrote "It's Quiet Uptown" using words that expressed how unfathomable it is to have a child pass away. Both Hamilton and Eliza coped with their devastation in their quiet terms—and in the end, they console each other reconnecting the two amid the soul-shattering grief.

## *"It's Quiet Uptown"*

At the time that Lin wrote and did the demo for "It's Quiet Uptown," a father and mother lost their son as well: Jack, Oskar and Laurie Eustis's son, passed away at 16 years old. Lin sent them an email with the recording, writing, "If art can help us grieve, can help us mourn, then lean on it." They listened to the song every day during the first week of mourning, and again as they walked in on the rehearsals at the Richard Rogers Theater, accepting everyone's condolences.

# Chapter 29: Containing a Dialogue on Ambition, and Some Topical Comments, from David Brooks and Christopher Hayes

When the election of 1800 came, Burr tied with Jefferson, and as fate would have it, Alexander was sought to be the deciding vote. Between a man who had no principles whatsoever, no firm stand on anything, a the politician who was the severe opposite of what *he* stood for, he chooses Jefferson—at least he believed in *something*, unlike Burr.

*New York Times* columnist and bestselling author David Brooks, and Lin's childhood friend, MSNBC host Chris Hayes, did not agree with Hamilton's decision—it would have been easier to work with someone pliable like Burr, someone "you can talk to." But Alexander was firm with his moral stand to a fault.

Both fans of the show, Brooks and Hayes agree that *Hamilton*, more than reflecting the politics of then and now, portrays the styles of ambition and how one achieves it the most American way.

## *"The Election of 1800"*

In this scene, Jefferson and Madison enter the stage, literally asking the audience if they can get back to politics after the crushing events in Hamilton's personal life.

This is where Burr leaps into action, campaigning actively to promote himself an approachable, non-elitist would-be president—which he tells later on that he learned from Hamilton.

As in history, Hamilton breaks the Jefferson-Burr tie by choosing Jefferson—something that the former French ambassador rubs in Burr's nose. This is the straw that breaks the camel's back.

# Chapter 30: Further Thoughts on Ambition, as It Pertains to the Playwright and the Enigmatic Burr

The "white whale" of the show was the final confrontation between Hamilton and Burr. In order to effectively dramatize the heaviness and monstrosity of what was about to happen, not only does Lin need to put himself in Alexander's shoes, but his opponent's, as well.

Burr was an enigma—and he described himself "a grave, silent, strange sort of animal, insomuch that we know not what to make of him." Much like his musical play counterpart, Leslie. The actor's calm, cool, and collected composure was a conscious choice, honed throughout the years. Onstage, he learned how to unleash Burr's anger as his own.

The exchange of letters between Hamilton and Burr in 1804 led to the fatal duel that would mark the latter as the villain in this part of history. Hamilton was the one person who always zipped past Burr on his way to the top—during the war, as lawyers, as politicians: Alexander was a hurdle to his success every single step of the way.

## *"Your Obedient Servant"*

This exchange becomes as scene of rapping passages from some of the letters between the rivals (again, with updated language), with a quick nod to *Parks and Recreation* ("Here's an itemized list of thirty years of grievance"), ending their messages with a sarcastic closing remark dripping with fury on Burr's part, laced with smug contempt on Hamilton's ("I have the honor to be your obedient servant").

## *"Best of Wives and Best of Women"*

A short moment between reconciled spouses, this song is Lin's homage to his own wife, Vanessa, who forced him to take trips so he could write outside the distracting life in New York; his first audience and critic, and the person who *does* wake up to find him writing.

# Chapter 31: How the Duel was Fought, and Rewritten, and Fought Again, as the Clock Ran Out

There was so much speculation surrounding what really happened during that fateful day in Weehawken: both seconds the in the duel claimed that the other side fired first—others say Alexander fired our of reflex when the bullet hit him in the abdomen (he rambled about his gun being loaded still as they rushed him to a doctor across the Hudson). The motivation that pushed Burr—was it blind rage? Or a choice made when he was backed into a corner, fearful for his life?

The show's collaborators waited to hear which one Lin would stick to as he wrote the final parts of the play—during the shows at the Public, he showed his decision *not* to take sides and leave the question hanging—something that Oskar did not agree with.

The meetings for script revisions were Oskar's opportunity to push Lin into telling the audience what made Hamilton, who declared that he was not going to throw away his shot during the first parts of the show, would suddenly do just that.

They ended up with a compromise: Hamilton *was* throwing

away his shot, but he hesitates. He evaluates his life. He worries over his choices even as he stood in front of Burr. As for his opponent, Lin chose to leave his motivation a mystery.

## *"The World was Wide Enough"*

The face-off between the long-time rivals begin with the same beats and tune as "Ten Duel Commandments," but with the rules already laid out before, it focuses on Burr's thoughts as they prepare, and Hamilton's right before the bullet hits him.

Alexander, the writer that he is, begins to make a list in rapid-fire verses: a revisiting of how he imagined death in "My Shot," his legacy, who was waiting for him on the other side, who will be left behind—he tallies his whole life before raising his gun to the sky and defiantly sings one line from "The Story of Tonight," "Raise a glass to freedom."

The narration swings back to Burr. An allusion to him reading *Tristram Shandy,* Laurence Stern's novel, later on in life (where someone catches a fly but lets it go, saying, "This world surely is wide enough to hold both thee and me.") is inserted. Burr's guilt-laden and regretful lines in the song were adapted from this snippet.

# Chapter 32: What is a Legacy? Or, a Sketch of Opening Night, and What Came After, and What Might Come Next

The opening of *Hamilton* on Broadway in August 6, 2015 was a hurricane—Lin's entrance as Hamilton had to pause for 27 seconds as the audience of 1,300 erupted. The performers dialed up their singing, dancing, and rapping.

The last song of the show was a rundown of Alexander's afterlife—how his enemies tried to discredit him, and how his beloved widow kept his memory and legacy alive, by ensuring that his papers were published, fighting slavery on his behalf, even opening the first private orphanage in New York City. The 50 years that she lived after losing her husband was spent telling his story.

After the almost-three-hour show, the team was transported by double decker buses to the after-party at Pier 60 at Chelsea Piers, along the Hudson River. The Roots were playing, Lin rapped onstage, Jeffrey brought in fireworks for the cast, crew, and their families who come from all over America to put together what Lin considers the tree from the seeds that Eliza planted, but never got to see grow.

## "Who Lives, Who Dies, Who Tells Your Story"

It was rare to end a show without the protagonist, but Lin took the cue from *Caroline, or Change*, where the last scene shows Caroline's daughter as she tells everyone how she'll do her best to honor her mother's sacrifices.

All pivotal characters surrounding Hamilton's life are present to tell what happened after his death—the way Jefferson, and Madison tried to discredit him, and how every single one of his enemies outlived him and his work—but there was one person who strived to continue it: Eliza.

She survived Hamilton for 50 years, and during those times, she attempted to collate his written works (though his biography was finished by his son after she passed away), had Angelica help her (and had her buried in Trinity church near Alexander; a sad final emphasis on how close they are, yet destined to be apart), raised funds for Washington's monument, campaigned against slavery, and her homage to her orphaned husband: the first private orphanage in New York.

A person's history and legacy lives based on who gets to tell the story: and Eliza did.

# Epilogue / Conclusion

On November 2, 2015, a special show was performed to help raise funds for the Democratic Party's presidential candidate, and President Obama took the stage to give his speech, while donors and the gaping *Hamilton* team listened.

It was a full circle closing: The White House was Lin's first ever platform for introducing the Hamilton project to the world, and the performance there boosted what would push and push the show to completion. And with its monumental success off and on Broadway, the show gets to now help the president.

As Obama stressed, "part of what's so powerful about this performance is it reminds us of the vital, crazy, kinetic energy that's at the heart of America—that people who have a vision and a set of ideals can transform the world."

## Final Thoughts

Hey! Did you enjoy this book? We sincerely hope you thoroughly enjoyed this short read and have gotten immensely valuable insights that will help you in any areas of your life.

Would it be too greedy if we ask for a review from you?

It takes 1 minute to leave 1 review to possibly influence 1 more person's decision to read just 1 book which may change their 1 life. Your 1 minute matters and we value it and thank you so much for giving us your 1 minute. If it sucks, just say it sucks. Period.

# FREE BONUS

## P.S. Is it okay if we overdeliver?

Here at Abbey Beathan Publishing, we believe in overdelivering way beyond our reader's expectations. Is it okay if we overdeliver?

Here's the deal, we're going to give you an extremely valuable cheatsheet of "Accelerated Learning". We've partnered up with Ikigai Publishing to present to you the exclusive bonus of "Accelerated Learning Cheatsheet"

What's the catch? We need to trust you... You see, we want to overdeliver and in order for us to do that, we've to trust our reader to keep this bonus a secret to themselves. Why? Because we don't want people to be getting our exclusive accelerated learning cheatsheet without even buying our books itself. Unethical, right?

Ok. Are you ready?

Simply Visit this link: http://bit.ly/acceleratedcheatsheet

We hope you'll enjoy our free bonuses as much as we've enjoyed preparing it for you!

# Free Bonus #2: Free Book Preview of Summary: Daring Greatly

## The Book at a Glance

In today's culture, people are more eager to seek success, power, and beauty. Having all of these things makes them feel special. As our nations continue to become industrialized, people, in turn, form higher expectations of each other. Unfortunately, these expectations usually entail sacrifices in terms of vulnerability and empathy. It seems that many are failing to remember that human beings should still be capable of feeling.

In schools, workplaces, and even at home, words that promote positive emotions and social connection are starting to decline. Young people throwing negative expressions toward each other is just another typical conversation we hear on the streets. Many people are not fully aware of how their words or actions can affect another's thoughts and behaviors. It's easy for them to degrade other people just to express their superiority. This leads to softness and vulnerability, once thought of as virtues, to now be perceived as weaknesses.

This book will enlighten you on the subject of shame and vulnerability. The first chapter will discuss the issue of not feeling enough or being enough. We spend a lot of time thinking of the things that we have, what we lack, and then comparing it with everyone else. We strive for perfection because that is what we see in the media. As a result, we feel shame when we feel as if we're not "catching up" to where everyone else is, all based upon the fact that we lack what they currently have.

The second chapter talks about the different myths regarding vulnerability. Sometimes, asking for help is seen as weakness. Instead of respecting this act of courage, we end up letting our fears turn it into a way of judging and criticizing others.

The third chapter will help you further understand shame and how you can resist it. We all experience struggles in life, but when we believe that we're inferior, it will start showing through our behavior. It stops us from recognizing our true strengths as human beings.

Whenever we feel fear or discomfort, we put on different kinds of shields and defenses to protect ourselves, the trouble with which is discussed in the fourth chapter. We are shown there that these forms of protection only make us grow wearier.

In the fifth chapter, you'll learn how protecting yourself from vulnerability can usually lead to disengagement, which is the fundamental problem in our society today. We are not perfect individuals, but we can learn how to engage more and align our values with our actions.

When it comes to education and work, the sixth chapter will discuss the importance of courageous leadership. Being a leader doesn't necessarily mean that you have a high-ranking position or a certain status. It's how you're able to combat shame through honest conversations.

Lastly, the seventh chapter talks about how parents can become good role models to their children by allowing themselves to be more vulnerable. Parenting is not easy and it can become frustrating at times. However, children tend to follow the ways of adults, which is why setting a good example is necessary.

In a world where people are full of expectations, we must not forget that we are still worthy of love and that we are enough. We must find the courage to accept our flaws and develop compassion for others and for ourselves. We live to connect with other people and having that connection is what makes life more meaningful.

# Chapter 1

## SCARCITY: LOOKING INSIDE OUR CULTURE OF "NEVER ENOUGH"

Once, while Dr. Brené was onstage for one of her talks, a member of the audience asked her why plenty of kids today think of themselves as special. A state of mind which, they say, often leads to narcissism. Here, the word was used as an all-inclusive label for other people's arrogant or rude behavior.

In connection with this thought, research was conducted to analyze several of the current most popular songs. The research reported a significant inclination toward hatred and narcissism in current and popular music. The words "we" and "us" are used on a smaller degree, while the words "me" and "I" are used on a greater extent. It also showed a reduction in words associated with positive emotions and social connection, as well as a surge in words connected to unfriendly behavior and anger, such as kill or hate.

It seems that we have become a culture full of self-centered people. Nowadays, people are more interested in gaining success, power, and beauty. We became so entitled, that we have deluded ourselves into believing our own superiority even when we really have nothing to contribute and nothing valuable to achieve. We don't have the much needed empathy in order to remain connected and compassionate people.

Sometimes, having an explanation for everything brings us relief. We hold other people responsible for the mistakes we made and we feel good about ourselves after doing so. Cutting the narcissists down in number is what we tend to think as the right cure. It's not important if they are our parents, teachers, our neighbors, or the CEOs of large companies. The reaction is still the same. They still need to be made aware that being special or great is not what matters most in life because chances are, no one would even care what we have accomplished in life.

Narcissism, as a subject matter, has already entered our awareness in such a way that people immediately link it with different behavioral patterns. This includes grandiosity, lack of compassion or empathy, and an extensive demand for approval and admiration.

What people don't completely understand is that the severity of a person's narcissism is actually rooted in shame. This means that trying to fix the problem by cutting down the number of narcissists is not the best solution, nor is it constantly reminding people of their smallness or inadequacies. *Shaming* people isn't the cure. It's what causes these kinds of rude behaviors.

### Understanding Narcissism in a Different Way

Pinpointing or labeling people who are struggling due to the things they're accumulating from their environment is often more disastrous to their overall healing rather than being actually helpful. The problem is that it focuses on who people really are instead of the choices they made. Dr. Brené believes that people must be held responsible for their own actions. However, she's not referring to **blaming** them, but pinpointing the main cause of the problems so they can be properly addressed instead.

It would be more helpful to identify behavioral patterns and to interpret what they might suggest. Understand how it's completely different from defining oneself by a specific judgment, and how lumping the two together usually intensifies shame and stops people from trying to seek help.

It's important for us to become aware of these influences and trends, but it's more beneficial if we view these behavioral patterns through the "vulnerable standpoint". For instance, when we see someone who's afraid of being thought of as ordinary — we must do our best to remove our biases. We can look at this from a place of empathy and instead, find someone who only wants to be noticed and loved. They're scared that being average would not give them that sense of belongingness or purpose which they desire.

This provides clarity and helps explain the root of the problem, as well as offer practical solutions. Nowadays, it's easy to believe this pervasive idea that our life is purposeless or ordinary simply because it is not expressed almost everywhere we go. We become susceptible to these kinds of messages which lead to destructive behavior, which also results in more pain and creates disconnection. Still, when we feel hurt and when our sense of love and belonging are at risk, we go after those that would give us full security.

The good thing is that, we can always learn something when we think about every information and expectation that determines our society, how these things affect our behaviors, the way our struggles are associated with defending ourselves, and the way they are connected to vulnerability.

Dr. Brené doesn't believe that the world is full of people who are narcissists. Our culture is just influenced by many different and powerful factors that people feel the need to overcompensate and create for themselves, a life that is beyond ordinary.

## Scarcity: The Problem of Never Having Enough or Being Enough

Scarcity simply comes with living. It's the issue of "never enough." It flourishes in a society where every person is extremely aware of insufficiency. We always think that we can never be enough. Everything feels limited or inadequate, especially when it comes to love, money, and security. We spend a lot of time thinking about the things we have and the things we lack and then compare everything with everyone else's.

We often compare our lives, families, marriages, or communities with unrealistic pictures of perfection, which are frequently conveyed by the media. But, what we don't realize is that this kind of behavior is completely useless and ineffective towards our own personal growth.

### Where Scarcity Begins

Scarcity doesn't seize a particular culture overnight. However, the feeling and idea exist in cultures that are prone to shame and are deeply filled with endless comparison and broken by disengagement.

We live in a world where life hasn't really been easy, but the recent years have brought with them many traumatic events, such as tragic natural disasters, numerous wars, school shootings and other random violence, that created a lot of changes in our society. We have survived, but we are constantly trying to make it through the things that have tattered our idea of security.

Falling into frustration with regards to scarcity is how our culture tries to cope with the stress. It usually begins when we've already been through so many things and instead of uniting to recover and improve, we choose to be angry and end up becoming paranoid.

It takes daily awareness, work, and commitment to develop relationships, raise a loving family, manage a school, or build an organizational system. This culture that surrounds us currently loves to put a pressure on us and if we're not willing to fight or stand up to the things we firmly believe in, we'll only end up suffering in scarcity

One way to prevent being in a state of not having enough is not acquiring everything or living in abundance, but rather living in wholeheartedness by believing that we're enough, we're worthy, and we can be vulnerable. We're all sick and tired of feeling scared. Each of us wants to make a bold and brave movement.

# SUMMARY:

# Head Strong

The Bulletproof Plan to Activate Untapped
Brain Energy to Work Smarter and
Think Faster – In Just Two Weeks

**ABBEY BEATHAN**

**Text Copyright © ABBEY BEATHAN**

All rights reserved. No part of this guide may be reproduced
in any form without permission in writing from the publisher
except in the case of brief quotations embodied in critical
articles or reviews.

## Legal & Disclaimer

The information contained in this book is not designed to replace or take the place of any form of medicine or professional medical advice. The information in this book has been provided for educational and entertainment purposes only.

The information contained in this book has been compiled from sources deemed reliable, and it is accurate to the best of the Author's knowledge; however, the Author cannot guarantee its accuracy and validity and cannot be held liable for any errors or omissions. Changes are periodically made to this book. You must consult your doctor or get professional medical advice before using any of the suggested remedies, techniques, or information in this book. Images used in this book are not the same as of that of the actual book. This is a totally separate and different entity from that of the original book titled: "Head Strong: The Bulletproof Plan to Activate Untapped Brain Energy to Work Smarter and Think Faster – In Just Two Weeks."

Upon using the information contained in this book, you agree to hold harmless the Author from and against any damages, costs, and expenses, including any legal fees potentially resulting from the application of any of the information provided by this guide. This disclaimer applies to any damages or injury caused by the use and application, whether directly or indirectly, of any advice or information presented, whether for breach of contract, tort, negligence, personal injury, criminal intent, or under any other cause of action.

You agree to accept all risks of using the information presented inside this book. You need to consult a professional medical practitioner in order to ensure you are both able and healthy enough to participate in this program.

# Contents

# Introduction

Most people think they're lazy, a bad person or a failure when they have bouts of forgetfulness, lack of focus, feeling fatigue and moodiness. They usually end up feeling frustrated, afraid and made life much harder than it really was.

We don't realize that the problem was that your brain was literally losing energy and wouldn't perform to the standards that you wanted. It seems that your efforts become futile because no matter how much you tried, you don't see any significant changes.

*Head Strong* will guide you on how to achieve a high-performance brain function. It gives you, the reader, tools to take control of your nervous system response and your cell energy generation. It gives people ways to reach their maximum potential so that they can do what they love to do. They can even do it better and with lesser effort.

By following the program detailed in this book, you'll be able to upgrade your brain in just two weeks and the results keep on building from there. You will experience more energy, clarity and better overall cognitive performance.

In *Head Strong* aims to equip you with the necessities to improve your brain performance

**Part I** delves on the brain, neurons, neurotransmitters and the mitochondria. It talks about the different brain weaknesses that people normally experience and suggest ways to address them. It looks into the mitochondria and the vital role it plays in keeping your brain cells healthy and your brain functioning well.

**Part II** outlines the right materials you need to keep your brain powered up. It talks about the nutrients you need and the foods you can get them from. It also talks about the benefits of light, air and cold, and the role that meditation and exercise play in improving your brain performance.

**Part III** gives suggested meal plans, lifestyle changes and supplements that can be taken to help you in the process. It outlines the key changes that need to happen in the two-week Head Strong program.

# Chapter 1
# Head Start

## Your Brain on Energy

Your brain works like your smartphone. When it was brand-new, it was fast and efficient but as you load it with applications and other data, it started lagging or stopped working as efficiently as it first did.

Your brain gets drained by your lifestyle: your diet and the environment around you. It gets poisoned by neurotoxins that destroy brain cells and functions plus the ability of the body to develop cells.

"Brain Kryptonite" includes anything, like certain foods you eat, types of light or exercise that pulls needed energy away from the brain and weakens it and redistribute it to other parts of the body. It doesn't immediately kill but slowly eats away your battery life.

Your brain needs tons of energy to work well. The mitochondria aptly called as the power generator of the cell creates the energy that sustains you and your bodily functions. Without which, can lead to your degeneration or even death. The number, efficiency, and strength of your mitochondria affect your susceptibility to degenerative disease or cancer.

Your brain's prefrontal cortex, the brain region implicated in complex cognitive behavior, has the most densely packed mitochondria which means that it contributes more to your brain's performance than the rest of your body.

When you're flooded with brain kryptonite, your body is unable to create or deliver energy as efficiently as it could. It is unable to meet the body's energy demand. This becomes visually revealed with fatigue. Fatigue is the ultimate performance killer. It causes being unfocused, brain fog, moodiness and forgetfulness. These are symptoms of an energy delivery problem and not a moral one.

Your body needs to make extra energy to get rid of toxins. But the toxins in your body makes it less efficient which, in turn, slows down the metabolizing and removal of the said toxin. This then requires the body to expend more energy to get rid of them. It's an unending, vicious cycle.

When you experience these symptoms of brain weakness, you probably associate it with your body's natural response to stress or an inevitable part of getting older. You probably got so used to having these symptoms that you learned to live with them or around them. You're redistributing your energy so you can still function.

This is conventional thinking. There are ways to change the amount of energy being delivered to your brain and this is what this book will touch on.

## The Three Fs

For a species to live forever, there are 3Fs that need it needs to be built in: fear things or using the "fight-or-flight" response, feed and get energy from food and the f-word for reproducing.

In the 1960s, Dr. Paul MacLean, a neuroscientist, and psychiatrist developed the "triune brain model" which is a simplified way of looking at regions of the brain for the study of the brain's energy use.

The 1st region is also called "reptile brain." This region is the first in line when it comes to energy needs, controls temperature regulation and other electrical systems. If you consistently don't get enough energy here, you will die.

The 2nd region is termed "Labrador retriever brain." This region controls the 3Fs mentioned earlier. This region controls the instincts, or the 3Fs mentioned earlier, that keep the species alive and propagating.

The environment where humans thrive has evolved. Today, our current lifestyle is bombarded with all kinds of stimuli

24/7 and it becomes difficult to distinguish between real and perceived threats. As such, the body is in a constant state of emergency – readily monitoring danger and reacting to even minor threats. Being this way eats up energy and takes our focus. When our energy dips it triggers the release of stress hormones that, in turn, will trigger urges to either run away, get distracted or give in to sugar cravings.

When you resist these urges, you're using the 3rd region termed "the human brain" or the prefrontal cortex which has a massive load of mitochondria. Every time you resist an urge, you are making a decision. The body is built to handle only a limited number of decisions before you reach "decision fatigue." Stretching the use of a fatigued brain often leads to bad decisions.

It is, then, suffice to say that being able to make good decisions is a good measure of brain performance. This book will outline strategies to turn down your "Labrador brain" and make your "human brain" stronger and more resilient.

Here's a four-step process that will help you do just that:

1. **Stop doing the stuff that makes you weak:** This will be difficult as we are surrounded by stimuli that slow down our brains. Identifying your personal kryptonite and removing it from your life will help free up your

brain reserves for more important things.

2.  **Add more energy:** Through strategic dietary changes and supplementation, you can ensure that your mitochondria will have the energy sources they need.

3.  **Increase the efficiency of energy production and delivery:** Through the removal of brain kryptonite, changing your diet and supplementation are the beginning steps of helping your mitochondria function better.

4.  **Strengthen your mitochondria:** By applying specific techniques to place the right amount of strain on your mitochondria and help it get rid of exhausted ones and stimulate the remaining ones to get stronger.

## The Five Brain Weaknesses

There are five common brain weaknesses tied to the mitochondrial function. You may have one or all of these weaknesses. It is difficult to identify but it's important to know where you're starting from to get the most out of the program. The descriptions below will help you identify the brain weaknesses that are impacting your performance the most:

**Weakness No. 1: Forgetfulness**

Short-term and long-term memory loss stem from the same causes: malnutrition, chronic low-grade bacterial or fungal problems, inadequate neurotransmitters and impaired mitochondrial functions.

A poorly functioning mitochondrion impacts other bodily functions that often leads to lesser energy produced for the body. The brain, then, is unable to get the energy supply it needs to work optimally and normally leads to memory blackouts. But once you fix your circulation and blood pressure, your brain's energy production will improve and so will the rest of the processes that are linked to it.

You'd also need to ensure that you have healthy neurons to transmit messages efficiency. Increasing BDNF or the brain-derived neurotrophic factor, the protein the survival of existing neurons in the central nervous system, encourages the growth of new neuron and their connections.

To determine if forgetfulness is a problem for you, see if you have experienced any of the following symptoms.

- Regularly forgetting names, important dates or events

- Asking questions repeatedly

- Increased reliance on memory aids

- Difficulty in tracking regular bills and regularly used items (keys, phone, etc.)

- Frequently losing your train of thought

- Forgetting a word or what you're doing in real time

So, how was it? If this sounds like you, you should pay more attention to the succeeding chapters on mitochondria functions, oxygen delivery systems, myelination, neurogenesis, and nutrition.

### Weakness No. 2: Cravings

These are physiological urges or biological cravings that signals that your brain needs energy.

Your mitochondria use oxygen to burn fat, glucose, or amino acids to make energy. If you eat too much sugar, your mitochondria will produce your energy requirement from glucose. Fat, which was supposed to be used by your brain as fuel, gets stored in your fat cells and you'll start gaining weight. Meanwhile, your brain will go thru the glucose quickly and cause your blood sugar to crash. This then alerts your inner Labrador that signals the alarm and starts a craving.

Cravings are a byproduct of an emergency signaled by the low supply of energy needed for the brain to perform optimally. To have an efficiently functioning mitochondria, you need to consume the right amount and type of fat so that the brain can build multiple energy pathways and not only reliant on sugar.

To determine if cravings is a problem for you, see if you have experienced any of the following symptoms:

- Frequent blood sugar dips

- Strong desire to eat something sweet after a meal

- Inability to go more than two to three hours between meals

- Irritability when hungry

- Exhaustion after spending time in a noisy environment

If these sounds like you, pay attention to the chapters on focus on light, environmental toxin and, ketosis.

**Weakness No. 3: Inability to Focus**

Do you find yourself unable to concentrate and often become distracted by thoughts, worries or even things in the environment around you?

When your brain is low on energy, it stimulates the release of cortisol or the stress hormone and adrenaline or the fight-or-flight hormone to make emergency fuel. The adrenaline breaks down muscle to access stored sugar reserves, which, in turn, signals your pancreas to release insulin needed to metabolize the sugar. The spike in insulin creates an even greater brain emergency. It heightens the process and makes you more unfocused.

To determine if the inability to focus is a problem for you, see if you have experienced any of the following symptoms:

- Wandering thoughts when trying to concentrate

- Difficulty in meeting deadlines and completing tasks

- Difficulty in staying organized

- Inability to multitask efficiently

- Inability to coherently hold a conversation

If this sounds like you, pay attention to the chapters on ketosis, meditation and breathing exercises.

**Weakness No. 4 Low Energy**

Do you feel tired all the time or do you find yourself moving slower than you'd like? Does your brain feel foggy like your hungover or jet-lagged even if you're not? If you have any one of these, you're probably suffering low energy.

The main culprit for low energy is poor blood sugar regulation. If your body is unable to effectively process sugar, your brain will be foggy and sluggish. To avoid this, you need to regulate your blood sugar by following a high-fat diet that teaches your body how to burn fat as fuel.

Another culprit is an inefficient mitochondrion. If your mitochondria are unable to produce energy efficiently, you'll always feel tired. This book has a program specifically designed to make the mitochondria more efficient in as little as two weeks.

To determine if low energy is a problem for you, see if you have experienced any of the following symptoms:

- Experiencing brain fog or lack of mental clarity

- Fatigue and muscle weakness

- Unsatisfactory sleep

- Extreme exhaustion after physical or mental exertion

**Weakness No. 5: Moodiness / Anger**

The prefrontal cortex controls your moods and requires the

most amount of energy to perform optimally. It is responsible for personality expression, decision making and moderating social behavior. Because of its massive energy requirement and the fact that its last in getting energy, this part of the brain usually suffers. A suffering brain can lead to uncontrolled mood swings and anger.

To determine if low energy is a problem for you, see if you have experienced any of the following symptoms:

- Impatience and snaps at people over minor things

- Gets unpredictable mood swings

- Volatile and sometimes violent behavior

- Has a history of impulsive and poor decisions

# Chapter 2
# Mighty Mitochondria

Your mother gave you all the mitochondria you need. Many people think that they receive an equal amount of genetics from their mothers and fathers but research shows that people are more genetically similar to their mothers. During conception, the mitochondria in the sperm get left behind as the sperm drops off its tail and burrow itself into the egg. Thereby, the mitochondrial DNA in a fertilized egg came exclusively from your mom.

Mitochondria are rod-shaped organelles, bound by a double membrane, with the inner membrane folded inside the outer one. Its role is to take glucose and use the energy stored in its chemical bonds to make ATP or adenosine triphosphate, a molecule that cells use as a source of energy.

Your mitochondria determine how your body reacts to the world around. So, if it's working efficiently, your mental performance increases.

## ATP – The Energy for Life

The most important thing your mitochondria do is extract energy from the food you eat, combine it with oxygen and make ATP.

ATP stores the energy required to power us physically and mentally. All cell requires ATP just to function. Its absence leads to severe degradation and even death.

When your body uses ATP as fuel it breaks down into two by-products: ADP (adenosine diphosphate) and P (phosphate). Energy is released when this happens. After releasing the energy, your body attaches the separated P (phosphate) molecule into the ADP re-creating the ATP. In essence, the mitochondria are using the same molecules to continuously generate energy.

The mitochondria are also in charge of transmitting signals between cells, cell differentiation and maintaining the cell lifecycle. Most importantly, all the critical systems in your body rely on mitochondria to work. These are essential structures that are not the least bit static. They are a part of your body that is constantly changing. They can be damaged, improved, renewed or hacked.

## Good Mitochondria Gone Bad

To know how to upgrade our mitochondria, we need to first understand what causes its dysfunction.

The most predictable cause of functional decline is aging. From age 30 to 70, the organelle decreases in efficiency by 50%. In short, a 70-year-old is making half the cellular energy of a 30-year-old which contributes to most symptoms and diseases attached to old age.

Mitochondrial function decline is inevitable but its deterioration rate may vary depending on your biology and lifestyle. It has also been theorized that one can keep its efficiency well into old age. The secret is to avoid early-onset mitochondrial dysfunction or EOMD by boosting your mitochondria now.

EOMD was discovered by Dr. Frank Shallenberger, a lecturer in one Silicon Valley Health Institution's talks. He defined EOMD as the deterioration of mitochondrial function in people below 40 and that 46% in that age bracket have it.

EOMD patients are asymptomatic. They have the symptoms we discussed earlier such as cravings and mood swings but don't feel sick. Over time, however, EOMD leads to accelerated cell death and loss, increased radical damage and mitochondrial decay.

EOMD is reversible. Decay is not. It manifests itself in four ways:

## Mishap No. 1: Inefficient Coupling

The core process your cells use to produce ATP is called the citric acid cycle or the Krebs cycle named after Hans Krebs, its originator.

Before the Krebs cycle can begin, the body converts protein or sugar into glucose, or fat into ketone body called BHB (beta-hydroxybutyrate). Both glucose and BHB provide carbon and electrons, the raw materials that create energy. Together they form a molecule called CoA (acetyl coenzyme).

Throughout the Krebs cycle, your mitochondria oxidize CoA creating carbon dioxide and electrons in the process. The electrons charge the NAD (nicotinamide adenine dinucleotide) then turns into NADH one of the molecules for energy generation.

The NADH donates its electrons to the electron transport system. There, molecules move electrons and proton across the inner mitochondrial membrane creating the power that drives ATP synthesis.

Protons and electrons work in pairs. Their attraction is used as a power source by putting a membrane barrier between them. If protons leak out, their partner electrons are left useless and then use up oxygen to get absorbed by your body.

Properly lined up protons and electrons avoid this energy wastage.

When you're suffering from coupling inefficiency, your mitochondria will burn up an excessive amount of oxygen to create ATP. All of the oxygen we breathe is used to produce energy in our body by burning fat or glucose. Without oxygen, your cells are forced to produce energy anaerobically. It is not as efficient and was theorized to cause cancer growths.

**Mishap No. 2: Reduced Recycling**

Your body recycles ADP by adding a phosphate molecule and when your mitochondria are not working properly, they use up ATP faster than they can be recycled from ADP. This leads to ADP buildup, a bottleneck in energy production then cell energy loss. Energy loss will require the cell to rest until more ATP can be recycled from ADP.

When this happens, your cells convert the available ADP into AMP (adenosine monophosphate), an inefficient and wasteful ATP alternate that cannot be recycled. It is an alternative but your body doesn't usually create it as it often just gets disposed of as urine.

Your body can also create a small amount of ADP directly from sugar by converting it to lactic acid. An issue though is that a build-up of lactic acid in muscles causes pain and soreness. It also leaves no glucose available for the body to use and no materials for ATP creation. This then starts the breakdown of the Krebs cycle.

**Mishap No. 3: Excess Free Radical**

An effectively working mitochondrion produces ATP efficiently and creates few free radicals. It also creates anti-oxidant buffering enzymes that neutralize free radicals before they do harm.

The inverse happens if it isn't. It produces an excess of free radicals that leaks into surrounding cells and have fewer free radicals to neutralize them. This wreaks havoc on your body and lays the groundwork for many degenerative diseases.

**Mishap No. 4: Poor Methylation**

Methylation is a mitochondrial process where a methyl group (1 carbon and 3 hydrogen atoms) are added to another molecule. This process controls genetic expression, inflammatory and immune response and energy production.

For the mitochondria, it creates the membrane that holds the electron transport system, creates amino acids for energy production, and creates ADP that converts to ATP.

If this process is impaired, your energy and ATP production get impaired too. This weakens your capacity to build energy from fat. Your body then relies on glucose for your energy source and your fat gets stored. This causes you to gain weight and since your body goes through the glucose fairly quickly, it will alert your Labrador brain to eat more sugar.

**Causes of Mitochondrial Dysfunction**

Here are the leading causes of EOMD and some of the ways that they can be fixed or prevented from happening:

- **Nutritional deficiencies:** Having the proper nutrient intake is one of the easiest and fastest ways to boost your mitochondrial function. The next few chapters will discuss the nutrients that it needs to function effectively.

- **Hormonal deficiencies:** Low thyroid hormones, high insulin spikes, and low steroid (testosterone and estrogen) hormones negatively impact mitochondrial efficiencies. For your mitochondria to perform optimally, you need to improve your hormone levels and keep your blood sugar stable. This book will tell you how.

- **Toxins:** Environmental and biological toxins are some of the leading causes of mitochondrial dysfunction. Environmental toxins such as toxic chemicals, pollutants, heavy metals such as lead and mercury hurt mitochondrial respiration and thereby impacting cellular energy production.

Your body naturally creates toxins that are as damaging as environmental toxins. Most of them are by-products of the energy creation process. The mitochondria produce anti-oxidants and other detoxifying enzymes to counteract these dangerous by-products.

However, defective mitochondria cause for these processes to malfunction. Oxidative stress happens if you don't have enough anti-oxidants to counteract the free radicals. Scientists believe that this is the cause of many diseases such as cancer, autism, Parkinson's and Alzheimer's.

Autophagy is the body's built-in detox process to recycle damaged cellular components. Boosting your autophagy process is one of the important things to improve your performance. This is also part of the Head Strong program.

- **Stress:** There are certain types and amounts of stress that are beneficial to your mitochondria. By temporarily stressing your body, you can boost your natural detoxification systems and stimulate the creation of new

135

mitochondria to maximize your energy.

But you have to make sure that you don't stress your cells too much as they can also have damaging effects on the cell cycle and begin apoptosis, or program cell death. Ineffective cells that have not gone to apoptosis will continue to replicate and often become cancerous or diseased.

Your mitochondria hold the signaling protein that induces apoptosis, so, boosting your mitochondrial function will help you hold on to healthy cells and get rid of the ones making you weak.

# Chapter 3
# Become a Neuromaster

## Own Your Neurons

Neurons connect to other neurons to create neural networks. These networks impact your daily performance: how you think, respond and learn. You are also partially in control of this process because you can change how your neurons will work.

There are two reasons why your neurons are a hackable part of your performance:

First, neurons use up massive amounts of energy for cellular engineering. Insufficient amount of ATP causes neural functions unpredictable or eventually die. So logically, if you can increase your ATP supply from the mitochondria then you can improve neural performance.

Second, neurons pass information from one end of their body to the other as a tiny electrical signal jumping across tiny gaps called synapses. They rely on neurotransmitters and a lot of mitochondria to fuel the process.

To ensure that the message can pass thru the synapses, your axons (or your neural voice) should be sufficiently protected by a fatty coating called myelin sheath which insulates the signal.

This neurotransmission process is the basis for how your brain functions and these networks are critical to your learning ability, memory and ability to focus. Ineffective processing of neurons negatively impacts all of these.

## How Your Neurons Can Perform Better

Myelin is a special, thick fat layer that is essential for your brain to function, without it neuron signals will be lost. Your oligodendroglia, a type of brain cell, is responsible for forming your myelin. Throughout adulthood, these cells constantly generate new myelin and replace those that break. To do this effectively, they rely on a proper balance of your thyroid hormones and progesterone.

Thyroid hormones affect mitochondrial function, ATP production and the survival of oligodendroglia cells and, in effect, the constant rebuilding of healthy myelin. It is then imperative to maintain your thyroid health and hormone levels always in check.

Progesterone hormones, usually associated with females because of its involvement in the regulation of menstrual cycle, signals your oligodendroglia to initiate the remyelinating process of neurons. It is also a prerequisite for sufficient testosterone production. Low progesterone levels can cause brain fog and other degenerative diseases.

In addition to right hormone levels, your oligodendroglia cells also need the right raw materials to rebuild myelin. Myelin is made of saturated fat, cholesterol, omega-3 and omega-6 fatty acids. Eating the right amount and type of fats is crucial in maintaining your myelin and keeping your brain signaling efficiently. Cholesterol deficiency is linked to cognitive function and memory decline, so, eating a diet that's high in the right kind of fats will increase memory and cognition.

There is also evidence that the right kind of temporary stress, particularly a fasting-mimicking diet, can improve myelin regeneration as well. Then, it is wise to conclude that a high-fat diet and a fasting-mimicking diet can separately help people with myelin decline and regenerate new ones. A combination of both will probably deliver extraordinary results.

The final way that you can advance myelin production is by improving how your brain communicates to your gut. Gut microbes play a significant role in brain function and how it is wired. There are initial results that show that there's a direct relationship between your gut bacteria and the myelin in your brain's prefrontal cortex. How exactly they impact the process is still being studied by scientists as of date.

## Building new Neurons

Neurogenesis is the process of creating new brain cells. This is an unending process in your lifetime. Your rate of neurogenesis is an important marker of brain performance. A low rate is often associated with cognitive decline, memory problems, and depression. A high rate, on the other hand, is related to cognitive enhancement, rapid learning, and resilience against stress and depression.

Studies have shown that it is possible to significantly increase the brain's state of neurogenesis. To help your brain do this, there are certain lifestyle choices and environmental factors that you need to manage for this to work:

- **Environmental Toxins**: Exposure to neurotoxins in your environment, such as heavy metals, solvents, additives or naturally occurring toxins from Mother Nature will slash your neurogenesis rate and kill off existing brain cells. They can also change how your neurons are using your neurotransmitters that are essential in brain function. The solution is to rid of those toxins and how to do that will be discussed in the next chapters. For now, just know that these toxins are detrimental to you.

- **Diet:** You can' make healthy and viable neurons without the right raw materials. To improve the rate of your neurogenesis you have to lessen your sugar intake that dampens it and then increasing the amount of omega-3 fatty acids to promote adult neurogenesis.

- **Bioflavonoids:** Plant compounds found in citrus fruits and many vegetables are effective in keeping neurons alive. Plant chemicals called polyphenols usually found in coffee, chocolate, and other blue, red and orange foods are also successful in growing neurons.

- **Stress and Depression:** For those suffering from chronic depression, taking antidepressants will boost the rate of neurogenesis which usually translates to more energy and better feeling.

  For those that are not clinically depressed, this is just a reminder to avoid chronic stress so as not to impair brain cell regeneration.

- **Exercise:** Exercise boosts your neurogenesis rate by increasing the blood flow to your brain and putting your body through short-term healthy stress. It also triggers the release of nerve growth factors that protect neurons from death.

- **A Fun Environment:** Enriched environments enhances neuron production. Expose yourself to different fun and engaging activities to aid the regeneration process.

- **Light and Water:** Drinking raw vegetable juices, fresh spring water or glacial meltwater will give you EZ water or exclusion zone water that is critical to mitochondrial function and its movement within microtubules.

    EZ water also comes from exposure to unfiltered sunlight every day. Exposing yourself to low-level light therapy and infrared saunas have the same effect.

- **Sex:** Studies have shown that having frequent sex can help enhance your rate of neurogenesis and buffer against harmful effects of cortisol.

Combining a high-fat, low-sugar diet with an enhanced detox strategy, an exercise plan and other stress-relief protocols are the keystones of the Head Strong program. Following this will definitely supercharge your brain as it makes new neurons along with healthy myelin.

# Chapter 4
# Inflammation

## The Muffin Top in Your Brain

Inflammation in itself is an important and useful physiological response. When a pathogen, toxin or trauma stresses the body, a short-term burst of inflammation is part of your body's effort to protect and heal you.

Inflammation only becomes a problem when it is chronic. With chronic inflammation, your entire body becomes inflamed and remains inflamed indefinitely. Your brain is the first to suffer when you are chronically inflamed because your brain is sensitive to inflammation anywhere in the body. Inflamed body parts release cytokine, a chemical that negatively impacts your brain.

Chronic inflammation is at the core of most-age related and life-threatening neurodegenerative diseases such as Alzheimer's, autism and even cancer. As an example, with Alzheimer's inflammation kills off neurons causing memory loss and other cognitive problems.

But it is not only old people that suffer from brain performance issues due to inflammation. Studies have shown that it actually affects brain performance at any age. This, simply, means that chronic inflammation is eating away at your mental acuity right now and if it leaves unchecked it'll take away your mental edge long before it causes you any physical pain or discomfort.

## What Causes Inflammation

Anything that irritates the body, including any form of physical or psychological stress, can cause inflammation. Inflammation is there to keep you alive so you can heal from an infection or injury.

It becomes problematic if it's turned on more often than necessary – which is the case for most of us. The world is filled with incessant stimuli, an overabundance of environmental toxins and unlimited access to artificially processed foods – these are factors that stress our bodies and cause inflammation which, in turn, reduces mitochondrial function.

The degree to which your brain is inflamed plays a huge role in how you feel daily. It can make you unreasonably angry, drive you to severe food cravings, distract you incessantly and make you forgetful even of the simplest things. Depending

144

on your genetics, your body may respond to inflammation by mounting an autoimmune reaction, which causes even more damage to your immune system as it attacks important system in your body.

## Inflammation and the Gut

Roughly 50% of the body's immune system is clustered around your digestive tract. Scientists believe it is designed this way because your stomach will probably come across over 20 million foreign molecules and your body would need to translate it into messages it can understand.

If your gut's immune system encounters something foreign to it, it sends out an alarm that activates inflammation throughout the body to deal with the threat. It usually manifests as a brain fog or bloating.

Your genetics and the microbes in your gut will impact how your body reacts to certain foods. It's important then to have the right gut bacteria on hand. Unfortunately, most of it is wiped out by antibiotics, pesticide-tainted foods, processed foods and unhealthy fats. This decline in helpful gut bacteria threatens the balance of immune systems and makes one more susceptible to inflammation.

In fact, low gut bacteria count can also cause Alzheimer's disease. Your gut bacteria create a short-chain fatty acid called butyrate that helps maintain the integrity of the blood-brain barrier. When your gut bacteria don't make enough butyrate, it makes the blood-brain barrier more permeable, allowing dangerous particles into the brain.

To prevent inflammation, one must maintain a delicate balance of gut bacteria – a combination of bacteria from the firmicutes family like lactobacilli and bacteroidetes.

Your body needs good bacteria like lactobacilli, you can get them from yogurt and most probiotic supplements. Too much of it, though, can cause inflammation. So, it needs to be balanced with a certain amount of bacteroidetes. You can't buy supplements for bacteroidetes probiotics but you can easily generate them by eating foods that contain their natural food source, polyphenols.

## Inflammation and Hormones

Hormone dysfunction causes inflammation and inflammation cause hormone dysfunction. It's a vicious cycle. The good news is that there are hormones that protect against inflammation. Some of these are:

- **Progesterone:** This is hormone critical for normal neural development. It is used to treat brain injury because it prevents neuron loss and regulates inflammation

- **Vasoactive Intestinal Polypeptide (VIP):** This is a hormone made in your gut, pancreas, hypothalamus and pituitary gland. It is critical in brain function as it protects against inflammation, controls nerve signals, regulates learning, immunity, and memory.

  Low VIP levels lead to a rise in blood sugar and insulin levels and start craving for more sweets. Reaching for a sugary snack can trigger a widespread inflammatory response that would, in turn, lower the production of VIP that you need to protect yourself from inflammation. Again, the vicious cycle begins.

- **Mammalian Target of Rapamycin (mTOR):** mTOR is not a hormone but it plays a vital role in controlling inflammation by regulating the cell's growth, survival, and death. The mTOR in your body increases energy production in your mitochondria and encourages its growth. But you have to keep the only the right amount of mTOR because an excess can increase your likelihood of developing cancer, obesity and other neurodegenerative diseases.

## Sneaky Fats

Eicosanoids are another class of molecules that can be controlled to help lower inflammation. These molecules act as messengers in the central nervous system, triggering an immune response after you invest something that your body perceives as toxic.

Eicosanoids come from omega-3 or omega-6 essential fatty acids. Omega-3 eicosanoids are anti-inflammatory while omega-6 ones are the reverse. Our bodies need a balance of both types to produce eicosanoids. But that balance is difficult to achieve. The sources of omega-6, like vegetable oil, is more accessible and more ingrained in our diets. This imbalance caused a dramatic increase in pro-inflammatory eicosanoids and increased inflammation alongside it.

The steady increase of sugar intake also added to this trajectory. It causes an insulin spike that triggers inflammatory cytokines. It also links up proteins, such as collagen, which in turn produces toxic AGEs (advance glycation end products). AGEs create oxidative stress in the body that triggers inflammation and, in effect, mitochondrial dysfunction.

When you consider all the ways that inflammation affects the body, it is apparent that nearly every cause of lowered energy production in your body now lays the groundwork for progressive deterioration in your performance and potential development of chronic disease later.

## Inflammation, Water and Light

In the earlier chapter, we discussed the importance of having enough EZ water in your cells. Your mitochondria need EZ water for it to function well.

The EZ water inside your cells is negatively charged to allow them to send a signal and communicate with another neuron. Inadequate EZ water levels lead to broken neural communication which, in turn, can lead to cognitive issues, depression, and other mood disorders.

The more negative charge your body has, the better your cells are able to function. Oxidation causes cells to lose their negative charge. So, your body activates antioxidants to fight excessive oxidation. It can do this by urinating, sweating and even defecating. All of these wastes are positively charged.

Light therapy is another way to help the body create EZ water. When regular water is exposed to infrared or UV light, or simply going outside without sunscreen or sunglasses, your body will soak up the light energy and build EZ water. Your eyes will serve as gateways for light to come in and directly make its way into your brain.

Light therapy has been proven to improve mitochondrial efficiency, increase protection from inflammation and hasten ATP production.

Exposure to the right kinds of light, feeding the good bacteria in your gut, balancing your hormones and improving mitochondrial function will help you lower your susceptibility to inflammation.

# Chapter 5
# Brain Fuel

Controlling your diet offers the easiest and most powerful way to improve your brain performance. Nutrition is the fuel that helps your brain run efficiently and causes it to break down. To keep yourself powered up, you need to have the right materials in you.

## Polyphenols: Brain-Boosting Anti-Oxidants

Polyphenols are antioxidants found in plants particular in dark red, purple and blue parts of plants. It helps protect the body against cellular damage from oxidation and offer other protective properties for the mitochondria. Here are some of its benefits:

- **Gut Protection:** Polyphenols and your gut bacteria have a symbiotic relationship. They change the composition of gut bacteria, in turn, your gut bacteria are responsible for metabolizing polyphenols so you can use them.

  Polyphenols can also protect your gut from dangerous pathogens such as staphylococcus and salmonella.

- **Increase Rate of Neurogenesis:** Polyphenols increase your levels of brain-derived neurotrophic factor (BDNF) and brain nerve growth factor (NGF) – proteins that promote neurogenesis and protect new neurons from dying off.

- **Determine Whether Cells Will Live or Die:** Polyphenols facilitate the cellular signals that start the process of apoptosis or cell death and prevent the mutation of old and damaged cells. Polyphenols keep your cells alive and healthy.

- **Fight Inflammation:** Polyphenols reduce the number of inflammatory cytokines in the bloodstream which increases mitochondrial function, enhances memory and prevents age-related decline.

Polyphenols have a lot of benefits but it is not easily absorbed by the body. This can be helped by consuming more fat. With the Head Strong program, you'll be eating lots of fresh dark veggies, low-sugar fruits and get the recommended number of polyphenols.

Aside from dark veggies and low-sugar fruits, there are other foods that offer the highest concentration of polyphenols:

- **Coffee:** This is the number source of polyphenol in the

152

Western diet. It contains different compounds that improve cell function. Coffee contains chlorogenic acid, a type of polyphenol that reduces chronic inflammation especially in cells with high-fat content such as brain cells.

Drinking coffee also lowers the risk of dying from common diseases including heart and lung disease, diabetes and infections. The positive impact is greater in women than in men.

- **Dark Chocolate:** 85% Dark Chocolate is full of polyphenols that enhances performance. But you still need to be careful when you ingest chocolate as it also contains mold toxins that inhibit mitochondrial function.

- **Blueberries:** Blueberries increase lifespan and slow down age-related cognitive deterioration. It also improves cardiovascular function and raise in BDNF too. Choose high-quality organic frozen or farm fresh blueberries for your polyphenol fix. Still be wary in eating blueberries as aside from polyphenol, you'll be getting sugar too.

- **Pomegranates:** These have water-soluble polyphenols that are more easily absorbed by the body. They are known to break down into smaller compounds that cross the mitochondrial membrane and fight oxidative stress

153

directly in the mitochondria.

- **Grape Seeds:** Grape seeds and extract are a potent anti-inflammatory. These contain proanthocyanin, a powerful polyphenol. Studies have shown that it corrects mitochondrial dysfunction caused by obesity. It is capable of correcting an energy imbalance and improving the fat-burning capacity of brown fat. Brown fat is the type of fat that helps you make energy and burn fat.

- **Grape Skins:** Grape skins produce a small number of polyphenols called resveratrol, it helps improve mitochondrial function, protect from obesity and insulin resistance caused by poor diet. You can get the same polyphenol in pistachios, blueberries and chocolate.

## Neurotransmitter Precursor Foods

Neurons need to communicate with each other and for this to happen efficiently, your neurotransmitters must function well. Neurotransmitters are produced in the gut and in the axons of brain cells. To function well, neurotransmitters relies on specific nutrients you ingest. If you don't have enough of these nutrients, it can lead a host of disease and a deterioration of your performance.

So, here's a list of neurotransmitters that impact your performance and the dietary sources you need to sustain them:

- **Dopamine:** This is an inhibitory neurotransmitter associated with the reward circuitry of the brain. Having sufficient dopamine levels positively impacts your decision making and overall performance. The scarcity of dopamine is linked to Parkinson's disease and social anxiety.

  Although drugs like cocaine and heroin increase the levels of dopamine there are far healthier ways to do so. One way is by exposing yourself to sunlight or a tanning lamp. Another is by taking foods that are high in the amino acids: L-tyrosine and L-phenylalanine.

  > **High in L-tyrosine –** beef, chicken, turkey, avocados, almonds

  > **High in L- phenylalanine** – wild salmon, sardines, bacon, beef, liver, almonds

- **Norepinephrine (noradrenaline):** This is an excitatory neurotransmitter that your Labrador brain needs to jump into action and help you form new memories. Dopamine is a precursor for norepinephrine so, you can eat the same foods as above. Just add on plenty of green veggies

155

and vitamin C supplement daily.

- **Serotonin:** This is an inhibitory neurotransmitter that directly impacts your mood. It also impacts perception and your quality of sleep. Low serotonin levels have been linked to depression, anger, and even suicide.

- **L-tryptophan:** Serotonin is originated from this neurotransmitter.

  **High in Tryptophan** - lamb, beef, chicken, turkey, wild salmon, mackerel, cashews, almonds, hazelnuts

- **Acetylcholine:** This neurotransmitter stimulates muscles, play a role in REM sleep, regulates temperature, and an extremely active in avoiding Alzheimer's disease. Low acetylcholine causes tiredness and light sleeping. Too much of it can cause jaw tension, muscle cramps and teeth grinding at night.

L-carnitine and choline are the precursors for acetylcholine. These are best absorbed when taken together.

  **High in L-carnitine** – beef, lamb, pork

  **High in Choline** – egg yolks, beef, kidney, liver, wild salmon

156

- **Gamma-Aminobutyric Acid (GABA):** This inhibitory neurotransmitter influences the development of new neurons, helps them become differentiated and form synapses. It is also known for its ability to calm the brain and reduce anxiety. Anxiety disorders such as panic attacks or seizures are associated with low GABA activity.

The precursor of GABA is L-glutamine. Foods high in glutamine are:

**High in L-glutamine** – beef, lamb, chicken, eggs, organ meats

Some of the foods overlap, its because they are the healthiest and most beneficial foods you can eat to help produce healthy neurotransmitters.

## A Fat Brain Is A Smart Brain

Fat has always been vilified. Throughout the years, people were told that low-fat foods were the "healthy" and better choice. Food manufacturers responded to this message by adding sugar to low-fat foods and the result was widespread obesity and health crisis.

When it comes to your brain, having the right fats is

important. A diet rich in healthy fats helps lower inflammation throughout your body and speed up energy production in your brain.

Still, a lot of are still uncertain especially when they hear that they should eat more fat. They link a lot of fatty foods with high cholesterol. Cholesterol is not an enemy. In fact, high-density lipoprotein or good cholesterol is beneficial to the body as it removes low-density lipoprotein or bad cholesterol from the bloodstream and helps maintain the inner walls of blood vessels.

There are two ways to understand fats:

First is to look at the length of the fat molecule. As a rule, the shorter the fat, the better anti-inflammatory properties it offers. Short and medium chain fats found in butter and coconut oil are the best sources of this kind of fats.

Second, it to look at how stable it is. Oxygen drives chemical reactions in the body and these reactions damage fats. Oxidized fats create inflammation in the body.

Luckily, your body uses many of the most stable fats to which it has access when making cell membranes. These fats are and their best sources are listed below:

- **Saturated Fats** – these have the fewest places for oxygen to cause damage and just enough damage-prone omega-3 fats to make membranes work.

**Best Source:** grass-fed animal fat and meat (bone marrow, lard, but not poultry fat), grass-fed beef tallow, pastured egg yolks

- **Monosaturated Fats** – these are the second most stable fats. They only have one vulnerable spot where oxygen can get in and wreak havoc.

   **Best Source**: Olive oil

- **Unsaturated Fats** – these are the least stable and most inflammatory type of fats but your brain still needs some of them. Omega-3 and Omega-6 are examples of unsaturated fats.

   Omega-3 fats are anti-inflammatory. The most important types of omega-3 fatty acids for your brain are EPA (eicosatetraenoic acid), a powerful anti-inflammatory and DHA (docosahexaenoic acid), the primary structural fatty acid in the human brain, retina and central nervous system. Breastmilk is rich in DHA essential for a baby's growing brain.

   **Best Source of Omega-3 Fatty Acids**: wild-caught, low mercury seafood such as sardines, sockeye salmon, anchovies and mackerel, fish/krill oil

## Ketosis is the Mostest

George Cahill, a scientist, learned that fasting prevents seizures by putting the patient into a state known as ketosis. In periods of severe carbohydrate restriction, the liver breaks down fatty acids and produce ketone bodies.

Ketones are water-soluble molecules that are the ideal fuel for the mitochondria. When ketones are used to create ATP, you're in a state of ketosis, a state of high performance defined by an increased mitochondrial energy output, reduced free radical production and increased GABA production.

Your brain's high performance can be attributed to the ketone bodies that are absorbed into the mitochondria wholly and undamaged. It made your body's process of releasing and recycling energy go faster. It becomes a more efficient process thereby using up lesser oxygen than burning glucose. It creates less oxidative stress as well.

The most common ways of getting into ketosis are to totally restrict carbs or to fast completely. You can also use brain octane oil to give your brain more access to ketones. It is a daunting task but the rewards are worth it. During your adjustment period, you will have bouts of fatigue, brain fog, and even bad breath. The bad breath comes from the burnt fat to create energy. Fat stores a lot of toxins and after processing released by your body. But over time, your body will get more efficient at running on ketones.

## Fasting for a Fast Acting Brain

Fasting is one of the ways to get into ketosis. Aside from that it also helps reduce inflammation throughout the body, enhances the myelination process, improves myelin regeneration and activates deep cellular detoxification process.

But fasting has its drawbacks – it can make you extremely irritable and cranky.

So, to experience the benefits of fasting, some people tried intermittent fasting where you eat your food within a specific window of time (about 6 to 8 hours) and the fast the rest of the day (about 16 to 18 hours). It was proven to be an effective way to cycle in and out of ketosis while remaining well fed and nourished.

If you experience an energy slump while fasting, get a cup of coffee. It is a great source of polyphenols. But it's better if its coffee made with the right beans, with brain octane oil and grass-fed butter – the ingredients of Bullet Proof Coffee. With this coffee, the energy lift is visible and brain function optimized.

# Chapter 6
# Brain Inhibiting Foods

There are certain foods that rob your body of energy. Here are some that you need to be wary of:

## Inflammatory Foods

Some food you eat cause inflammation by irritating the lining of the gut and triggering your immune system to attack healthy cells and have a negative impact on your brain. Unfortunately, it's not easy to know which foods are causing inflammation. Still, you can do this simple test at home to find out. It's not precise but it will give you a good enough picture to see how your body reacts to certain food.

If you're going to eat something that you think might be causing a problem, take your heart rate before a meal and several times after. You'd have a guilty suspect if your heart rate significantly increased after the meal.

Even if inflammatory foods vary per person, there are some foods that cause inflammation to nearly everyone. Here are the top offenders:

- **Trans Fats:** These fats are born when hydrogen is added to liquid vegetable oils to make them more stable. Food manufacturers use these fats in their products because they have a longer shelf life than other fats.

Trans fats change the composition of the mitochondria and build up inside it as they are metabolized. They cause inflammation to your brain and put your immune system in hyperdrive.

Excessive consumption of foods rich in trans fats, such as baked goods, fried foods, and potato chips, is connected to host of illnesses including cancer, dementia and Alzheimer's disease.

- **Dairy Products:** Milk is made up of water, protein, sugar, and fat. Milk protein causes inflammation. It binds to the good polyphenols in your diet and makes them unavailable to your body and, in essence, your mitochondria.

- **Gluten:** Gluten is a protein usually found in wheat that causes digestive distress to many people. When you eat gluten-filled foods such as bread or pasta, your body is prompted to release zonulin, a protein that controls the space between the cells that line your digestive tract. Excessive gluten intake lead zonulin overload that pushes cells further apart leaving more room for pathogens to pass thru the gut's protective lining and in the end cause inflammation.

Gluten also reduces blood flow to the brain and interferes with the thyroid hormones that you need to create ATP, myelin and healthy mitochondria.

- **Vegetable oils:** All vegetable oils are inflammatory and provide an overabundance of omega-6 polyunsaturated fats. Vegetable oils are extremely unstable that they easily oxidize in heat, light or air. The excess omega-6 causes an imbalance that triggers inflammation.

## Toxic Food

There are two types of toxins in your food: manufacturer added ones such as preservatives and artificial flavors, and naturally occurring toxins that plants, bacteria, and fungiform to protect themselves. But whether they're artificially created or naturally occurring, both can make your mitochondria weak and cause inflammation. Listed below are some of the worst toxins out there:

- **Mold toxin (mycotoxins):** This toxin is naturally occurring in many foods and environments. Exposure to mold toxins is detrimental to your health – specifically to your mitochondria. Sadly, most people don't know when they've been exposed to toxic mold.

At low exposure levels, the impact manifests in subtle effects that make one feel like "they're having an off day", "feeling cranky" or "needing more sleep." Basically, exposure to small amounts can make you sluggish and distracted. But high levels of exposure can cause serious illnesses such as cardiomyopathy, cancer, kidney disease and brain damage.

OTA (ochratoxin A), a type of mold found in high polyphenol foods such as coffee, chocolate, and grains, is pure mitochondrial kryptonite. It interferes with apoptosis, causes oxidative stress and weakens the mitochondrial membrane. It is also an immune suppressant and makes you more susceptible to various auto-immune diseases.

Here are the common sources of toxic mold:

o **Cereals and Grains –** Mold grows on harvested grains because of improper handling and storing. It accumulates moisture which, in turn, invites mold to grow. This then is either directly manufactured as your daily breakfast cereal or fed to animals before they were slaughtered.

o **Coffee –** Studies have shown that more than 90% of coffee beans were contaminated with mold before processing. On average, decaf coffee contains even more mold toxin than caffeinated ones because producers use lower-quality beans for decaf and removing caffeine leaves the beans defenseless against mold that form in beans if stored improperly.

o **Dried Fruit –** Dried fruit contains loads of sugar than regular fruit and the drying process creates high levels of mold toxins. Aside from drying, some dried fruits are sprayed with chemicals such as sulfites that harm your mitochondria too.

o **Wine and Beer –** Beer gets its OTA from grains. Fermentation lower the OTA concentration but not eliminate it. Wines are also contaminated with OTA. Grapes get this toxin through the crushing process.

o **Chocolate –** Like coffee, chocolate is a great source of polyphenol but can are also a source of mold toxins.

o **Nuts –** Nuts are likely sources of mold toxins.

Nuts with the lowest risk of exposure are those that were purchased with their shells. Its suggested to buy whole nuts with skin and stored in the fridge.

o **Corn –** Fusarium, the most common corn fungus, creates a toxin that inhibits mitochondrial functions. Industrial farming has been treating farm soil with antifungals that the fungus now lives on the roots of the corn plants making it invisible to the naked eye.

o **Artificial Sweeteners, Flavors and Additives –** As it is food already has inflammatory properties, it is worsened by manufacturers by using all sorts of chemicals in food processing to make them taste better and extend their shelf life.

o **Monosodium Glutamate (MSG) –** Of all the additives manufacturers use, MSG has the worst impact to cognitive performance. It is an excitatory neurotransmitter that keeps your neuron incessantly firing for no good reason. This is called excitotoxicity and causes your neurons to run out of energy, create free radicals and then die. It makes you weak and causes

167

chronic neurodegeneration.

- o **Aspartame** – This is an artificial sweetener made up of amino acids. One of these is phenylalanine, which is chemically altered to form free methanol that is neurotoxic and converts into formaldehyde in the liver. Formaldehyde causes oxidative stress, reduces cellular energy production and apoptosis.

  It is also an excitatory neurotransmitter like MSG.

- o **Soy Sauce** – Soy sauce is usually fermented with Aspergillus, a type of fungus that contains citrinin, a mold toxin that induces apoptosis. Soy sauce contains tyramine and histamine, stimulating neurotransmitters, which causes oxidative stress, excitotoxicity, and mitochondrial damage. It also contains MSG and gluten that are both detrimental to mitochondrial function.

- **Neurotoxins:** These compounds ARE mitochondrial kryptonite that can impede performance even in the smallest amounts. Most common sources of neurotoxins are:

168

o **Fluoride** – Fluoride reduces thyroid hormone that your mitochondria need to function and maintain healthy myelin.

o **Genetically Modified Organisms (GMOs)** – GMOs are universally sprayed with a class of pesticides known as organophosphates. Low levels of exposure are linked to adverse effects in the neurobehavioral development of babies and children. They tend to have lower IQs and problematic learning capacity.

It is suggested to buy organic at the grocery store or acquaint yourself with a local farmer and buy goods directly from them.

• **Mercury** – This is a heavy metal that depletes the antioxidants that your mitochondria need to combat oxidative stress. Mercury is commonly found in seafood. It accumulates in the fish tissue so the higher a fish in the food chain is, the more likely it contains dangerous levels of mercury.

• **Sugar** – When you have high levels of blood sugar and insulin, your body releases inflammatory cytokines. This starts a vicious cycle as insulin causes inflammation and inflammation causes tougher insulin resistance.

All forms of sugar are bad for your brain but fructose is the worst. It creates oxidative stress and feeds the bad bacteria in your gut, leading to even to more inflammation.

- **Alcohol** – This causes oxidative stress in your mitochondria while simultaneously weakening its oxidative stress defenses. Alcohol slows down the cell's energy production, weakens them and often leads them to death.

## Good Fats, Gone Bad

Aside from choosing healthy food options, one must also look at how these foods are prepared. When you smoke, fry or grill meat you create two carcinogens: HCAs (heterocyclic amines) and PAHs (polycyclic aromatic hydrocarbons). These compounds don't only cause cancer but they are neurotoxic and induce tremors.

Another problem with some cooking methods is that they damage important proteins. Damaged proteins are considered "heat-denatured" which aren't necessarily toxic but they also can't perform their jobs well.

The worst damage cooking brings is the destruction of fats by oxidizing them. Your myelin and hormones are made of fat. Your mitochondria rely on fat to function. If your body is made of damaged fats it becomes less flexible and functional.

Listed below are some of the top offenders to cooking fats:

- **Frying:** Anything fried is full of damaged fats. The process of deep frying bathes your food in oxidized fats and denatured proteins. It also produces PAHs and HCAs that further compounds its toxicity.

- **Safflower and Sunflower Oils:** Both oils are prone to oxidation. But sunflower oil has a lower smoke point and has higher proximity to oxidation.

- **Vegetable Oils, Soy Oils, Corn Oil and Trans Fats:** These oils and fats are prone to oxidation, triggers inflammation and impedes mitochondrial function.

- **Barbequed Meat:** The fats in this delicious meat was converted into carcinogenic and inflammatory HCAs and PAHs.

This chapter was not meant to scare you but to make you

understand the huge impact of food and how you handle it can have in your brain function. The goal is to arm you with knowledge so that you can take charge of everything you put into your mouth and help you make smarter and healthier choices.

# Chapter 7
# Avoid Toxins and Improve Your Body's Detox System

Detoxing is important in optimizing brain performance. Your body has an innate detox system that can rid of toxins on its own but not all of it. The assortment of naturally occurring and man-made toxins assaults our bodies far more than it can reasonably handle.

Removing toxins from your life is not easy. You can start by simply avoiding toxic foods that you read in the previous chapter. But it doesn't end there, there are non-food sources as well – in the air, in your home and even your medicine cabinet,

But to better prepare, you listed below are toxins that you need avoid and suggestions to start detoxing from the ones that are hurting your brain.

## Environmental Mold

Molds create mycotoxins, chemical toxins naturally occurring in many foods and environments. It does not matter whether you're exposed to low or high levels of these toxins as they are extremely detrimental to your health.

The impact of mycotoxins depends on the following factors: the type and amount of mycotoxin you're exposed to, the duration of exposure, the other toxins present in your environment, and your personal health profile including your age, sex, genetic background, and lifestyle. All these factors play in identifying your susceptibility to the mold's negative impacts.

Mycotoxins are naturally occurring, so, it's impossible to completely avoid them. But logically, you can surmise that the more you get exposed to it, the more chronically inflamed you'll be. Eventually, your immune system becomes hypersensitive to the threat and responds even to the tiniest presence of mold toxins. This response is commonly known as allergies.

Toxic mold is also present at your home. In the 70s most buildings were made with drywall which absorbs moisture which creates an ideal environment for mold to grow. Mold is kept at bay by adding fungicides in the paint. Unfortunately, the mold outsmarted us, mutated and created a fungicide-resistant strain that makes even more mycotoxins.

Mold once it grows in your home, school or office quickly spreads and contaminates everything else around you – your furniture, clothes and other belongings. Moving is not the solution as you just might be taking the mold with you as you move.

This is why you need to protect yourself and, in essence, your brain. The steps will help you avoid mold and recover from its effects if you've been exposed:

- **Avoid Water-Damaged Buildings:** Avoid living, working or attending school in any building that has been damaged by water from a flood, broken pipes, or water leaks until a licensed mold specialist has remediated the building. Water stains on the walls or funky smell are tell-tale signs of mold presence.

- **Prevent, Identify and Repair Water Leaks:** Keep your drains, toilets, and pipes in good working conditions to prevent flooding. Have your pipes professionally checked for leaks and if found, repair them immediately.

- **Consider Safer Building Conditions and Materials:** Pay attention to the building materials used when buying or renting a new home. Inspect the new home for an intact moisture barrier in the walls.

- **Ensure Proper Ventilation:** Make sure there's good ventilation in your home, school or office. Poorly installed air-conditioning units and HVAC (heating, ventilating and air-conditioning) systems in hot, humid climates may post a risk.

- **Have your home professionally inspected:** Hire a professional to perform a complete test of the interior and exterior of your home.

- **Remove and Remediate Mold:** If testing shows that you have toxic mold from your environment, remove yourself and work with a remediation specialist to develop a clean-up plan.

- **Detox Your Diet:** Focus on a diet low in sugar, rich in antioxidants and polyphenols, and containing high-quality fats, grass-fed protein, and responsibly sourced foods. Doing this will supercharge your mitochondria to help you deal with mold exposure. Supplementing your diet with mitochondrial-enhancing supplements will help you make energy and aid in detoxification.

## Heavy Metals

Your mitochondria are sensitive to heavy metals like mercury, lead, and nickel. Even a small amount and short duration of exposure to these toxins are sufficient to impair

176

mitochondrial energy production and instigate its death.

Here are some of the most common heavy metals:

- **Arsenic:** This heavy metal is used to manufacture chemical compounds like pesticides and herbicides, and to manufacture different types of paint, glass, and metal. Arsenic is a known carcinogen and is also a neurotoxin that impacts mitochondrial function and causes various neurological problems.

- **Lead:** This heavy metal was commonly used in paint until the federal government banned it. Lead exposure leads to decreased mitochondrial function, damaged neurotransmitters and led to cognitive impairments like brain damage, convulsions and lack of motor coordination.

- **Mercury:** Signs of mercury poisoning includes fatigue, depression, irritability, loss of memory, and headaches. Long-term impact can include nerve degeneration, tremors, and permanent brain damage.

## Pharmaceutical Drugs

The Food and Drug Administration (FDA) does not require pharmaceutical companies to establish whether or not a medication approved for sale can harm your mitochondria. But scientific tests have proven that most of these medications are either directly or indirectly toxic to your mitochondria. What's worse is that your mitochondria are very sensitive to the effects of these medications compared to other parts of the body.

When scientists develop drugs, they consider how it will impact various bodily systems but often neglect to fully consider the impact on the brain. It may be helping you in other areas but you may end up impairing your performance.

Listed below are drugs that affect your mitochondria. If these medications are doctor prescribed, it is best to discuss the urgency of taking that medicine and the effects they may have:

- **Antibiotics:** Common antibiotics are now proven to cause mitochondrial dysfunction. Studies have shown though that taking the antioxidant glutathione with it can help your body protect itself from the harmful effects of antibiotics.

- **Beta blockers:** These medications cause oxidative stress which damage the mitochondria.

- **Barbiturates:** Phenobarbital decreases the number and size of your mitochondria.

178

- **Anti-Inflammatories and Cholesterol Medication:** Inhibits the Krebs cycle making it more difficult for your mitochondria to produce energy.

- **Anti-depressants, Antipsychotics, Antivirals (Interferon), Anti-Arrhythmics Diabetes and Cancer Medications:** All these medications cause mitochondrial dysfunction and death.

## Detox

Your body already has a natural detoxification system that's meant to process and eliminate toxins. And there are several easy things that you can do to help your body's detoxification processes. First, you can make sure that your body has the substances it needs to run efficiently. Another main way is to encourage the natural detox processes like sweating to help break down fat cells. Here's a list of other methods you can do to boost your detox system:

- **Sweat in a Sauna:** Anything that makes you sweat will help you naturally detox. Exercise is a way to do it but the sauna is faster way to shed toxins. Remember to hydrate while you use the sauna to detox.

- **Burn Fat with Exercise:** Exercise makes you sweat and

179

increases the breakdown of fat tissue which help release toxins stored in fat tissues. It also improves circulation that creates better oxygen flow to your liver and kidneys so they can filter out toxins.

- **Chelation Therapy:** This involves an intravenous injection of compounds called chelators that bind to toxins in the bloodstream so you can pass them normally. This therapy is effective in removing heavy metals. But there's still some risks involved with this therapy so talk to your doctor before attempting this one.

Toxins are inevitable and scary. They can cause a lot of harm so one must take active steps to avoid them in one's environment and eliminate from one's body. The Head Strong program will aid you toward fast detoxification, efficient energy production, and supercharged mental performance.

# Chapter 8
## Your Brain on Light, Air and Cold

Biohacking is the art of changing the environment around you so that you'll have full control of your brain and body. Light is one of the important factors that play a critical role in signaling the mitochondria.

Generally, light directs your mitochondria on what to do and when to it. To do that, your eyes need huge amounts of energy for visual processing. When you have an unstable energy supply to the mitochondria in your eyes, you can suffer from brain fog, headaches and difficulty to perceive shades of grey.

Fortunately, you're in control of the type of light in your environment. There are many ways to improve mitochondrial function. Here are some suggestions:

### Junk Light is as Bad as Junk Food

Today, people are more exposed to a lot of unnatural-spectrum light or "junk light." Junk light is from newer artificial lights like white LED (light-emitting diode) and CFL (compact fluorescent light) bulbs that lack many of the frequencies that our bodies and brain need.

We are supposed to absorb sunlight into our cells and our mitochondria. But in our quest to save energy, we've created artificial light and removed natural light sources such as infrared lights, UVA (ultraviolet A) and UVB (ultraviolet B).

Infrared light is invisible to the human eye but you can experience it as heat. It is necessary to most living things.

UVA and UVB both come from the sun and have positive biological benefits. But today we block out these frequencies with UV-filter windows and sunglasses or block them with sunscreen. Although it right to block out some UV rays especially with its supposed connection to cancer.

But the fact is, your body needs some UV light to function properly. UVB is vital in activating vitamin D and help set your circadian rhythm, the process that tells you when to sleep and wake up. You can take vitamin D supplements but you need actual sunlight to activate it.

One of the biggest issues with junk light sources is the amount of blue light they emit. The new white LED light bulbs only appear white but they emit at least five times more blue light than you find in nature, they're completely infrared-free and red spectrum-free that are found in natural sunlight.

Blue light has a lot of negative effects on your mitochondria. First, it needs to work doubly hard to produce the energy it needs to process LEDs blue light. It burns through oxygen and creates free radicals in the cells of eyes that, in turn, stresses the mitochondria in your eyes and later on your brain.

Blue light also changes mitochondrial shapes and creates stress protein linked to macular degeneration or the deterioration of the central area of the retina often resulting in blindness.

Furthermore, blue light increases free radical production but not activate the cleanup signal to increase antioxidant production. Excess free radicals stay in the cell member resulting in macular degeneration and decreased energy production.

Aside from free radicals, it also reduces NAD in the mitochondria in your eyes. Without sufficient NAD your cells are unable to complete the Krebs cycles and produce energy. It will lead to weakness and sometimes change your eye shape and cause nearsightedness.

With all these disadvantages, the best way to go is to cut down your exposure to blue light and increase your exposure to high-quality light sources to balance the excess bad ones you get. Sunshine is still the best, so if you can, spend a little bit of time in the outdoors.

## Red Light Means Go

Your mitochondria are meant to experience red light all day, with less blue at the start and end of the day. When we spend time outside, we're exposed to full-spectrum light. But in today's lifestyle is spent indoors where we get lots of blue light. Your mitochondria pay the price.

To balance the excess blue light you get, you can place simple red LED lights around your home and your office, switch to halogen lamps and get some quality outdoor light exposure throughout the day. Your skins must have direct access to natural light in order for you to reap the benefits of infrared light.

You can also spend time in an infrared sauna to help your body detoxify, rest your eyes and produce EZ water.

## Visual Kryptonite

Another hack is to reduce the amount of visual kryptonite its exposed to. Visual stimulation like high glare and contrast stresses your brain and leads to headaches, irritability, and inability to focus. The reason you feel this is with high glare and contrast your brain needs to work harder to process information.

Some of the ways you can address this are by changing your light settings on your computer screens and mobile phones. You can install f.lux to control the colors of your computer screen. You can also use orange sunglasses that block blue light. These small adjustments can help you get your energy back.

## The Air Up There

Breathing is a unique biological function that naturally happens voluntarily or involuntarily. Breathing happens automatically but you can also intentionally alter your breath by speeding it up, slowing it down or stopping altogether. This gives you the best window to improve your performance.

One of the suggested ways to increase the amount of oxygen in the body is by temporarily stressing your mitochondria through restricting your oxygen intake for short periods of time. Doing this causes your mitochondria to grow stronger or die, or help it become more efficient at using oxygen when present it is present.

During, short periods of low oxygen intake or hypoxia increases the production of BDNF that helps support neural growth and development. Improved oxygen delivery will energize your cells and make you resilient in situations with limited oxygen intake.

To get this result, you can apply this breathing technique that provides short bursts of oxygen to cells and trains them to use oxygen efficiently:

First, sit down, get comfortable, and close your eyes. It's best to do this right after waking up since your stomach is still empty. Warm up by inhaling deeply and drawing the breath in until you feel a slight pressure. Hold the breath for a moment before exhaling completely, pushing the air out as much as you can. Hold the exhalation for as long as you can, and then repeat these fifteen times.

Next, inhale through your nose and exhale through your mouth in short, powerful bursts, as if you're blowing up a balloon. Pull in your belly when you're exhaling and let it expand when you inhale. Do this about thirty times at a steady pace. You may feel light-headed or you may experience a surge of energy that's literally electric.

When you're done, take one more big breath in, fill your lungs to maximum capacity, and then push all of the air out. Hold this for as long as you can and try to feel the oxygen spreading around your body. When you can't hold it anymore, inhale fully and feel your chest expanding. Hold it again, sending energy where your body needs it.

186

## The Benefits of Brain Freeze

Cold thermogenesis is a type of cold therapy that uses cold temperatures to create heat in your body. Thermogenesis is a process that burns fat and stimulates the release of proteins that burn glycogen from your muscles. When your muscles are depleted of glycogen, your body receives a signal to increase testosterone and growth hormone introduction which in turn leads to reduced inflammation, increased insulin sensitivity and stimulate autophagy.

Cold therapy can improve thyroid and mitochondrial function stimulates the release of the neurotransmitter norepinephrine which helps relieve pain and signals your body to produce more antioxidants, particularly glutathione.

It also helps you tone your vagus nerve also known as the "wandering nerve." It starts at the brain stem and travels throughout the body connecting your brain to different organs like your lungs, heart, liver, and kidneys. It is a vital component of your parasympathetic nervous system which is responsible for calming you down after an excitable response.

People with high vagal tone tend to have healthier blood glucose levels and more consistent energy. Conversely, people with low vagal tone are more likely to have chronic inflammation.

In summary, light, air, and temperature are vital components of life on Earth. Biohacking these elements offer opportunities to enhance performance and supercharge energy and brain power. Following effective protocols that limit your exposure to junk light, reduce visual kryptonite and stimulate positive cellular changes through cold therapy, will give you better-quality sleep and more energy than ever before.

# Chapter 9
# Sleep Harder, Meditate Faster, Exercise Less

By working with your mitochondria instead of against them, you can improve your sleep, get more out of meditation and see better results from your workouts. Doing the Head Strong program will not use all of your free time or energy, in fact, it will give you more of it. This is how:

## Sleep Harder

When you sleep, your body may be resting but your brain is not. It goes into a janitorial mode. Your glymphatic system performs the overnight detoxication maintenance work for you.

Your glymphatic system sends clear cerebral spinal fluid through the brain's tissue, effectively flushing out cellular waste and neurotoxins from the brain and transporting them to the circulatory system. Then they go to your liver and be processed as waste.

Your glymphatic system is highly active during sleep because it takes a lot of energy to circulate its cleaning fluid

189

throughout your brain. At this time, your brains shrink by as much as 60% - this makes it easier for the fluid to circulate through your brain tissue. After it has been cleaned, the cells return to their regular size. This shrinking and growing are powered by your mitochondria.

You can turbocharge your brain's maintenance system and get cleaning up done in less time if your mitochondria are working efficiently. It's a positive chain of reciprocity: the more efficient your mitochondria are, the better your glymphatic system can operate, and the better-quality sleep you'll get. With quality sleep, you'll have better-performing mitochondria because they'll be freshly scrubbed clean.

## Meditation for Calmer, Happier and Shapelier Mitochondria

Studies consistently support the advantages of meditation. It has shown that meditation changes the brain on a structural level. A regular meditation practice yields visible results – you develop more folds in the outer layer of the brain, a trait correlated with intelligence across species.

Meditation also thickens areas of the cortex and insula, regions of the brain associated with complex thought, concentration and problem-solving. It also reduces levels of stress hormones cortisol and adrenaline thereby reducing inflammation and calming your inner Labrador so you can focus and be emotionally stable even in the most challenging situations.

Meditation also reduces hypertension, infertility, and depression. These reductions are attributed to enhanced mitochondrial production and utilization. Better utilization brings about mitochondrial resiliency.

The best way to meditate is in conjunction with technology that can provide instantaneous feedback.

- **EEG (electroencephalogram)** neurofeedback is one of the most effective tools to do just that. With neurofeedback, a practitioner applies sensors to defined points on your scalp that monitor your brain waves and send them to a computer. The computer then converts your brain waves to sounds or images that give you a visual or audible representation of what's happening in your brain as you meditate.

- **HEG (hemoencephalography)** is a type of neurofeedback that focuses on increasing blood flow to the prefrontal cortex. To do this, you strap a sensor to your forehead and then think happy

191

thoughts. When you do it right, blood rushes to the frontal lobe. The sensor detects the change in blood flow, and it provides feedback. This is effective for people suffering from ADHD.

- **40 years of Zen** is an intensive, five-day, all-day program designed to put you in the same state of mind as an advanced Zen practitioner who's been practicing meditation for decades. It is an extreme form of neurofeedback and is not accessible to everyone.

## Exercise Your Brain

When you exercise, it stimulates the release of essential proteins that are beneficial to mitochondrial health:

- **PGC-1 alpha (peroxisome proliferator-activated receptor-gamma coactivator-1 alpha):** helps to regulate metabolism and mitogenesis. Like sleep, it is not the quantity but the quality of exercise that's important.

- **FNDC5 (fibronectin type III domain-containing protein 5):** part of this protein goes into the bloodstream and increases levels of BDNF in the hippocampus where neurogenesis happens.

Scientists discovered a link between PCG-1 alpha and BDNF. Increasing PCG-1 alpha raises FNDC5 production which then leads to even greater BDNF increase. This then led to the birth of new neurons and new mitochondria.

Exercise also lower mTOR protein which your body help weed out dysfunctional cells, lowers your blood sugar levels and make you more sensitive to insulin. It also improves circulation, reduces inflammation and allows more oxygen to pass through to all your tissues, including your brain.

- **Functional Movement:** You don't need to go to the gym to benefit from exercise. All you need to do is move. Walk, hike, ride the bike, do yoga, jump rope or run around the playground with your kids will stimulate neurogenesis.

  It is essential then to move. If you're confined to a desk job, find some time within the day to get up and move around. You can simply walk around the office as your exercise.

  Or you can also practice yoga. Yoga helps people stay focused, take in and retain new information. Yoga also

193

incorporates cross-lateral movements or movements in which one of your limbs crosses the center line of your body, that increase blood flow to all parts of the brain. Your left and right hemisphere are also working together at this time.

- **Resistance Training:** This involves pushing against a force that resists movement. Some examples of this training type include weightlifting, kettlebell training, and body weight workouts. They're short and intense, these short bursts of stress are beneficial for your brain and body.

  Resistance training aids the body's natural detoxification process significantly decreases anxiety, improves memory and cognition, reduces fatigue and boosts the endorphins that make you happier.

  But you have to be careful not to overtrain as it causes for your cortisol to rise and your BDNF to drop. With the Head Strong program, you'll do resistance training once a week and plenty of movement on other days.

- **Endurance Training:** This training is more commonly known as cardio or aerobic exercise. It relies on oxygen from your lungs to produce energy. Anything that makes you breathe heavily such as running, swimming or biking stresses your aerobic system and tests your endurance.

Endurance training boosts BDNF levels permanently and it is the best way for your body to release endorphins.

- **High-Intensity Interval Training (HIIT):** HIIT workouts alternate between intense strenuous exercise and brief periods of active rest. HIIT is an efficient way to train without requiring much time to have your workout.

HITT is a marriage of resistance and endurance training. It subjects your muscles and your cardiovascular system to extreme stress and then allows them to recover during the active rest period. This rest period keeps your heart rate elevated so that you can still reap the benefits of a good aerobic exercise.

## Exercise and Water

You already know that EZ water is essential for your mitochondria. Shaking water molecules which is a natural result of most forms of exercise creates EZ water. This benefits not only your mitochondria but all cell membranes.

Cell membranes are made up of small droplets of fat suspended in water. When these tiny drops of fat are shaken, it creates a piezoelectric effect which allows materials to generate an electric charge in response to stress. This effect creates EZ water in your cells and allows them to do their job more efficiently.

High-vibrational movements are the best to shake up water. You can do it via mini-trampoline, jump rope or jumping jacks. There are tools to help too: BulletProof Vibe and Atmospheric Cell Trainer (ACT) were both designed to cause your cells to expand and contract to create a piezoelectric effect.

## Melanin and Water

Melanin is the pigment that makes our skin dark. It is also in our eyes and our brains. Scientists observed that when melanin is exposed to sunlight or mechanical vibration, it gains the power to break water apart, freeing oxygen and electrons for your mitochondria to use and make energy.

We can make melanin by linking polyphenols together. This means that the more polyphenols you eat, the more melanin you can make.

Now that you know the triggers you need to pull to optimize your brain performance, its time to put them into action. The next two weeks will be your introduction to the Head Strong program where you will learn how to eat to fuel your mitochondria, detox from harmful toxins and maximize the benefits of light exposure, breathing, proper workout and quality sleep.

# Chapter 10
## Eat to Fuel Your Brain

Before starting the program, it is best to dedicate a day or two to shop and source high-quality ingredients. Connect with a local farm or go to a farmer's market to find great product and grass-fed animal products. If that is not an option for you, source organic, local produce and grass-fed meat from grocery stores in your area.

To start here's a shopping list for two weeks:

- **Proteins:** Gelatin, Pastured Eggs, Pastured Bacon, Ground Grass-Fed Beef or Lamb, Pastured Pork or Lamb Leg/Shoulder, Ground Bison, Wild Salmon Fillets, Sea Scallops and Wild Alaskan or Cold Smoked Sockeye Salmon

- **Fats:** Brain Octane Oil, Grass-Fed Ghee and Butter, Coconut Milk (Full Fat, BPA and guar gum free), Coconut crème, Olive Oil, Avocados

- **Herbs and Spices:** Sea Salt, Xylitol, Vanilla Extract, Sage, Fennel Seeds, Cayenne Powder, Oregano, Rosemary, Mint, Cilantro, Basil, Fresh Ginger, Shallots, Cumin, Coriander, Thai Basil, Turmeric

198

- **Veggies:** Cauliflower, Broccoli and Broccoli Sprouts, Red Bell Peppers, Leeks, Asparagus, Carrots, Iceberg Lettuce, Zucchini, Cucumbers, Romaine Lettuce, Celery, Thai Chilies, Lemongrass

- **Fruits:** Frozen blueberries, Shredded Coconut, Tomatoes, Lemons, Limes, Blackberries, Raspberries

- **Nuts:** Pistachios, Almond Butter, Pistachio Butter

- **Miscellaneous:** Upgraded Bulletproof Coffee, Upgraded Collagen from Grass-Fed Cows, Macha Green Tea Powder, White Rice, Apple Cider Vinegar, 85% Dark Chocolate, Chocolate/Cocoa Powder, Gluten-Free, Grain-Free Bread or Crackers

Here are some recipes for the Head Strong Program.

## Breakfast: Brain Sunrise

This is an easy to make breakfast that will give you ketones from the Brain Octane Oil and healthy fats from the avocado, eggs and bacon for your cell membranes and myelin. This meal will keep you satisfied until lunch. This recipe only serves 1.

*Ingredients:*

2 – 3 strips pastured bacon

1 – 2 eggs from pastured chickens

2 Tbsps. Apple cider vinegar

½ organic Hass avocado

1 Tbsp. Brain Octane Oil

Himalayan sea salt and fresh herbs to taste


*Directions:*

1.  Preheat the oven to 320°F.

2.  Bake the bacon in a roasting pan or a baking sheet for 10 minutes, turning the bacon over once. Keep the bacon fat. If you don't have an oven, you can cook the bacon

on a stovetop, low and slow is the way to go.

3.  Poach the eggs in water that has been combined with the apple cider vinegar. Stir the water before cracking the eggs so the eggs stay in the center of the pan.

4.  Thinly slice the avocado lengthwise. Arrange the pieces in an arc across the plate, and then place the bacon around the rim. Arrange the poached eggs at the base, like the sun peeking up over the horizon.

5.  Mix 1 tablespoon of the conserved bacon fat with the oil. Drizzle this energy ambrosia over your Brain Sunrise. Garnish with some salt and fresh herbs, and serve with black coffee, green tea, or no-sugar hot chocolate for polyphenols. Save any leftover bacon fat and store in the fridge for use in future dishes.

# Lunch: Green Mind, Clear Mind Macha Bowl

This is a non-traditional meal great for day when you're too busy to deal with cooking. It contains high amounts of polyphenols and collagen. This meal only serves 1.

*Ingredients:*

1 ripe organic Hass avocado

1 peeled organic Persian cucumber or ½ organic English cucumber

½ coconut cream

1 tsp. Macha green tea powder

1 – 2 Tbsp. Brain Octane Oil

5 mint leaves

2 Tbsps. Bulletproof Collagen

Stevia

¼ cup pistachios or more

Shredded coconut

Handful of mint sprigs for garnish

## Directions:

1. Place the avocado, cucumber, coconut cream, tea powder, oil, and mint leaves in a blender and blend until well combined. Next, add the collagen. Just blend it enough to mix it in and no more. Be careful because over blending can degrade the collagen. Then add stevia to taste and stir.

2. Pour the mixture into a bowl. Sprinkle the pistachios and shredded coconut liberally on top. Garnish with mint sprigs.

3. Eat with a small teaspoon to prolong the pleasure of texture and color and taste. Pay attention to the distinct and steady lift in energy you feel as you eat.

# Dinner: Bacon-Ginger Scallops with Cauli Rice

This dish has everything your brain needs – omega-3s, polyphenols, anti-oxidants and deliciously healthy fats. You can replace cauli rice with white rice if you need more carbs. This recipe is for 2 – 4 diners.

*Bacon-Ginger Scallops Ingredients:*

3 Tbsps. grass-fed butter or ghee

10 stalks of lemongrass

1-inch piece of fresh ginger, peeled and finely grated

1-pound wild sea scallops, tendons removed and patted dry (no need to rinse)

8 pcs. of thin-cut bacon

1 tsp. ground turmeric

*Cauli Rice Ingredients*

1 head of organic cauliflower

2 Tbsps. unsalted grass-fed butter

2 Tbsps. Brain Octane Oil

Sea salt

1 head of organic romaine lettuce

1 cup broccoli sprouts

4 stalks of organic celery, sliced

*Directions:*

For the *Bacon-Ginger Scallops:*

1.  Preheat the oven to 320°F. Put the butter, 2 stalks of chopped lemongrass (the white part), and the ginger in a medium saucepan.

2.  Heat over low heat, stirring often, for 20 - 30 minutes or until the flavors have infused. Make sure the mixture does not boil!

3.  Once infused, remove the saucepan from the heat. Place the scallops in a small bowl. Pour the mixture over the scallops.

4.  Wrap a piece of bacon around each scallop and secure each with one of the lemongrass stalks.

5.  Set the scallops on a rimmed baking sheet, sprinkle with

turmeric, and place in the oven. Bake for 8 - 15 minutes, checking often, until the bacon is crispy. The cooking time will depend on the size of the scallops.

6.  Remove the lemongrass toothpicks before serving.

For the *Cauli Rice*:

1.  Grate the cauliflower or use a food processor to pulse it to the right texture so that it resembles rice.

2.  Heat a large sauté pan over medium heat and melt the butter. When the butter melts, add the riced cauliflower. Cook it gently for 5 to 10 minutes stirring and turning over often. Be careful as you don't want to brown the cauliflower.

3.  Once the cauliflower is cooked through, turn off the heat, add the oil, and season with salt to taste.

4.  Serve with the scallops and a romaine lettuce side salad that's topped with broccoli sprouts and sliced celery.

# Dessert: Raspberry Chocolate Pudding

This is a rich, indulgent and nutrient rich dessert that sharpens your cognitive performance plus its delicious too! This serves 2 – 4 people.

## *Ingredients:*

4 cups full-fat coconut milk, BPA-free and guar gum–free

Up to 4 Tbsps. xylitol or stevia

2 Tbsps. Bulletproof CollaGelatin or 1 Tbsp. gelatin

2 tsps. vanilla extract

¾ cup Bulletproof Chocolate Powder

4 Tbsps. unsalted grass-fed butter

1 Tbsp. Brain Octane Oil

¼ cup pistachio nuts (optional)

½ cup organic raspberries

Shaved 85% organic dark chocolate

## *Directions:*

1.  In a small saucepan over medium heat, heat 1 cup of the coconut milk, the xylitol, and the gelatin until the gelatin is dissolved. Place the remaining 3 cups of coconut milk in a blender with the vanilla, chocolate powder, butter,

and oil. Blend thoroughly. Add the hot coconut milk/gelatin mixture to the blender and pulse until mixed, with or without the pistachio nuts. Pour out the mixture into a large bowl and let it set for 1 hour.

2.  Serve the pudding in small coffee cups, covering the top of each dessert with a halo of raspberries. Then use a carrot peeler to shave the dark chocolate in generous curls over the raspberries before serving

# Snacks: Midday and Sleepy Snacks

## Midday

When you find yourself having an energy slump midday, have one of these snacks for a quick pick me up:

- 1 oz. 85% dark chocolate

- Head Strong Quick Bites: Place one or more of the following toppings on a piece of grain-free bread or grain-free crackers 1 Tbsp. grass-fed butter; a slice of wild smoked salmon; ¼ avocado, mashed.

## Sleepy Time Snack

To supercharge your sleep, try this Head Strong Tea recipe before going to bed to give your cells the energy they need to stay powered all night long.

*Ingredients:*

1 cup chamomile tea or other herbal tea, such as mint

1 Tbsp. Brain Octane Oil

1Tbsp. raw honey

*Directions:*

Cool the tea, then blend in the oil and honey and enjoy. If you're not a tea person, try mixing the oil and honey together with collagen for a quick nightcap.

# Chapter 11
# Head Strong Lifestyle

Eating healthy to fuel your brain is just the beginning. Including minor changes to your light and cold exposure, sleet, meditation and exercise habits will support you and your mitochondria in the process of achieving better brain power. For the next two weeks, implement the changes below and see the positive results yourself.

## Let There Be Light

You should avoid junk light and make sure you're exposed to the right light frequencies at the right times of day.

- **Block LEDS:** Go through your house and cover all of the blue, white and green LEDs you can find. You can cover it with electrical tape or TrueDark dots that are designed for this purpose. These block the harmful light frequencies.

- **Maximize your Technology:** You spend a lot of time staring at your screens. To avoid taxing your mitochondria while you do, install f.lux from getflux.com. It's a free software that you can adjust your blue light output settings for day and night. You can do this for your computers and your smartphones too.

- **Dim the Lights:** Install dimmer switches in your bedroom, living room and any other areas where you spend time before bed. Dim your lights at least two hours before bed or turn off most of the lights in your house especially white LEDs. Dimmer lights will tell your body to start producing melatonin so you can wind down and go to sleep.

- **Set-Up a Sleep Cave:** When sleeping, follow these habits:

  o It's essential to make your room as dark as you can. Block all light sources, use blackout curtain or just pinned up fabric.

  o Turn off your alarm clock or get rid of it.

  o Try using candles in the evening instead of electric lights. If you need a night light, make sure it's a red or amber one.

- **Look (and Feel) Like a Rock Star:** To complete the rock star look, you can use cheap amber safety glasses available online or the TrueDark glasses from biohacked.com. You can still see when you're wearing these glasses but your biology believes your sitting in the dark. This, in turn, will help your brain create more melatonin.

- **Protect your Skin from Junk Light, Not Sunlight:** When you're going to be locked up inside at home or in the office, wear long sleeves to give your skin and mitochondria a break. Bring out your polos and shorts if you'll be outside. Its better to get rays from the sun and not indoor lighting.

- **Balance with Healthy Light**: In the morning, go outside for at least a few minutes without sunglasses. Show a little skin to help create vitamin D3 sulfate. At night, red is your color. Minimize sources of blue and white light. Use red or amber bulbs whenever possible.

## Exercise Your Way to A Better Brain

To maximize the brain benefits of exercise, there are three components to focus on: meaningful movement, high-intensity interval training (HITT) and resistance training.

- **Meaningful Movement:** This could be yoga, a hike or a dance party. The objective is to just get moving and keep moving. Keep the movement to a moderate intensity. It's better to do it outdoors so you'll also get the benefits of light while exercising. Doing this 3 – 5 time a week will be very beneficial to your body and of course, your mitochondria.

- **HIIT-Back Exercises:** At least once a week, go outside and run for 400 yards. Run like your being chased, be as fast as you can, like your life depends on it. Then do something lazy like sitting down on a bench or lie on your back for ninety seconds. Then repeat one more time. Doing this will let your nervous system (and mitochondria) have more time to completely recover.

- **Resistance Training:** Plan a once a week resistance training workout to raise BDNF and stress your mitochondria. To save time, you can do resistance training after your HIIT exercises.

Perform one set of these five compound movements for each session. Make sure to move from one movement to another without so much break in between:

1. Seated Row

2. Chest Press

3. Pull Down

4. Overhead Press

5. Leg Press

## Hack Your Sleep

Follow these simple steps to get the best-possible quality sleep that will help your mitochondria clean house during the night so you can wake up fresh and ready for the day.

- **Switch to decaf after 2:00 PM**: Caffeine affects your sleep cycle. Stay off the caffeine at this point and drink decaf.

- **Don't Work Out Before Bed**: Doing your HIIT and resistance workouts 2 hours before sleep will keep you energized and up all night. Instead, you can do relaxing yoga to help you wind down.

- **Hack your Sleep with Honey**: Have 1 Tbsp. of raw honey before bed on an empty stomach. Raw honey replenishes your supply of liver glycogen so you can create stable glucose levels for long periods of time.

- **Go to Airplane Mode**: When you go to sleep, turn off your Wi-Fi router and put your phone in airplane mode or leave it in another room while you sleep. This will protect you from EMFs and any lights or sounds your phone might make during the night.

- **Breathe**: Perform a simple breathing exercise before bed to lower cortisol levels and turn off your fight-or-flight response to help you sleep. One type of breathing exercise is the box breath.

Sit down in a comfortable chair with your feet on the floor and your hands in your lap or do it in bed lying flat on your back. Close your eyes and mouth, and slowly breathe in through your nose as you count to four. Hold your breath for another count of four and then exhale through your mouth for an equal final count. Finish up by holding your lungs empty for the same count. Then repeat several times.

## Mitochondrial Meditation

Meditation is an exercise built around increasing and controlling the mitochondria. This meditation will focus on opening up the pathway from your body to the ground. With focused breathing, you can reconnect with the earth's energies and bring it back to your body.

Practicing meditation once a day throughout the two-week program will give you the maximum benefits. The audio meditation is available on the Head Strong website.

## Cool Off

Every morning at the end of your shower, turn the water all the way up to the coldest setting for the last thirty seconds. Stand there and let the water hit your body, face and chest. This shower is both energizing and relaxing. Performing this trick before bed every night will drop your body temperature and help you sleep deeply at night.

# Chapter 12
# Head Strong Supplements

You don't have to take supplements to make your mitochondria strong but there are some that can help make things more possible and help you overcome obstacles that are preventing your mitochondria from making maximum power.

## High Impact Supplements

These are the most powerful supplements for the mitochondria.

- **KetoPrime:** This is a new, stabilized form of OAA (oxaloacetic acid) packaged in lozenge form along with co-factors that allow the OAA to do its job in the mitochondria. It mimics the impact of restricting calories, increases the precursor NAD+ and protects the brain from excessive glutamate.

- **Glutathione:** This is your body's master anti-oxidant in your liver. It protects the body from oxidative stress and heavy metal damage. You can either take glutathione intravenously or you can swallow special forms that bypass your stomach digestion. IV glutathione works best but it pricey and can be a tad inconvenient.

- **ActivePQQ:** PQQ (pyrroloquinoline quinone). PQQ improves mitochondrial density, function, and biogenesis. It functions as an anti-oxidant, protecting against inflammation and oxidative stress, it boosts metabolism and improve learning capacity.

  BulletProof Unfair Advantage is the only product on the market today that delivers the active form of PQQ that bypasses your stomach acid.

These supplements are optional. But you will definitely notice a huge difference in the way you feel by just following the meal plan, start better habits and take some supplements to push your performance further.

# Chapter 13
# Beyond the Limits

Chapters 10, 11 and 12 have outline activities for the two-week Head Strong program. If you like the positive impact of doing the two-week program and want to take it to an even higher level, the hacks in this chapter are for you.

## Deeper Sleep Hacks

Hopefully, with the tips detailed in Chapter 11, you're already getting better-quality sleep than before. Listed below are other tricks to get you a deeper, restorative state of sleep:

- **Magnetize Sleep:** The mitochondria are semi-conductive and magnets affect the energy production in each cell. Transcranial magnetic stimulation was designed to take advantage of the relationship between magnetic fields, the brain and sleeping. It stimulates the brain's production of serotonin, melatonin and other neurotransmitters needed for a good night's sleep.

  To receive the stimulation, you hold a device containing an electromagnetic coil against your forehead while short electromagnetic pulses are administered through the coil.

The magnetic pulse easily passes through the skull and causes small electrical currents to stimulate nerve cells in the targeted brain region.

- **Sleeping on a Bed of Nails:** A Bulletproof Sleep Induction Mat stimulates acupressure points. Activating your points allows relaxation to flood your body and lets you drop into a parasympathetic state. It helps you get into deep sleep quickly, increase blood circulation and endorphin release as you sleep through the night. In the parasympathetic state, your mitochondria go to work and repair.

## You are What's Around You

Your body is both electric and chemical. It responds to chemicals, electricity as well as light, sound, air and water. There are other ways that your bodies respond to your environment. Here are some that you may be aware of:

- **Stimulate your brain:** Running a current over your body adds more electrons to your system so that you can make energy quickly. Electrical stimulation can either be done via CES (cranial electrotherapy stimulation) or tACS (transcranial alternating current stimulation).

CES runs an electrical current back and forth your brain to put your entire brain in the same state while supercharging the mitochondria.

tACS uses a computer that shapes the exact electrical waves that can change your brain activity the most.

- **Ozone Therapy:** The ozone is made up of 3 oxygen atoms. The third oxygen atom supercharges oxygen into ozone and gives it powerful healing properties. Ozone regulates the immune system, treats autoimmune disease, stimulates cells to take up more oxygen, and helps the mitochondria.

There are 3 types of ozone therapy you can try:

  o Major autohemotherapy (MAH or MAHT). Blood is drawn intravenously, then mixed with ozone gas and reintroduced to your veins.

  o Insufflation is where you take a measured volume of specific-strength ozone gas and put it in your body either vaginally or via your rectum.

  o Prolozone is the kind of therapy where a physician injects ozone gas and some nutrients into an injury site like a knee or spine. It lowers swelling and turns on healing.

- **Cryotherapy:** Find a cryotherapy center near you where you can get cold in a safe and controlled environment. You'll stand in super-chilled air at -270 degrees Fahrenheit for about 3 minutes. That 3 minutes will get your mitochondrial fully energized and recharged.

- **Light It Up:** Try out a far infrared sauna. It transforms the water in your cells into EZ water so your mitochondria will work efficiently. You can start at about 20 – 30 minutes, 2 – 3 times a week. The amount of time you spend will vary depending on your fitness levels and other health factors.

  You can also use infrared LEDs or red LEDs to recharge your mitochondria. It is more effective than a sauna with almost no sweating. Do this for at least 20 minutes daily.

- **Shake, Bounce and Vibrate:** Include other activities to your Head Strong workout routine like jumping on a mini trampoline for 5 – 10 minutes daily to shake off the water in cells and increase your EZ water levels. Tai chi and yoga with body-shaking exercises can have similar effects.

- **Get grounded:** Walk outside barefoot for a few minutes every day to allow the extra electron to flow into the earth. This will help you feel more energized, improve sleep and reduce inflammation.

## Beyond Supplements

The Head Strong recommended supplements boost your brain function. There are other mitochondrial stimulants that can improve your performance exponentially.

- **Nicotine microdosing:** Nicotine when taken in low doses of its purest form, without toxins and carcinogens wrapped around it, is a formidable bio hack that directly effects your mitochondrial function with a low risk of addiction. It gives you more precise motor function, makes you more vigilant and focused. The suggested dose is 1 – 2 mg of nicotine occasionally. Take it on an ad hoc basis and treat it carefully.

- **Methylene Blue**: Before it was used as a dye during diagnostic tests. Then scientists found that blue dye increased oxygen flow to different parts of the body, particularly the brain. It can cross the blood-brain barrier and acts as an anti-oxidant in the brain. If you're an athlete, have chronic fatigue syndrome or other mitochondrial disorder that's hurting your quality of life, its ok to experiment and try this.

- **Smart Drugs**: Racetams are some of the oldest cognitive-enhancing pharmaceuticals on the planet. The author recommends Aniracetam is a fat-soluble version of this drug that is documented to improve memory and phenylpiracetam that give you more energy.

## Train Your Eyes and Ears

Your sight and your hearing require energy to deal with the information they receive.

- AIT (auditory) integration training – this is a special ear training to address brain drain due to auditory stress

- Irlen lenses – visit a local Irlen practitioner and get fitted for a custom pair or Irlen lenses to filter out the frequencies of light that your brain does not like. You can also check out TrueDark glasses in the Head Strong website.

## Stem Cells – The Future of Biohacking

Stem cells are special cells that have potential to turn into many other types of cells. Stem cell treatments are cutting-edge treatments for multiple sclerosis and other mitochondrial degenerative diseases. There are still ongoing studies to find out other ways to use stem cells to affect mitochondria. But one day, scientists may be able to find ways to successfully transplant mitochondria from one person to another.

# Conclusion

By this time, you would have fully understood the benefits of boosting your mitochondria to your overall performance. You also learned that:

- Your brain needs enough energy to function well and this energy is produced with the help of the mitochondria.

- Dysfunctional mitochondria can lead to fatigue, inability to focus and retain memory and a lot more cognitive deterioration diseases.

- Dysfunctional mitochondria are caused by a concoction of environmental and man-made toxins. Prolonged exposure to huge amounts of these toxins can damage your neurons, weakens your mitochondria, slows down energy production and fuels inflammation.

- But this can be addressed by removing these toxins from your environment. You can do that by smartly selecting organic produce and grass-fed meat products. Removing unhealthy fats and sugars from your diets will also help.

- Toxic mold is everywhere. It is detrimental to your mitochondrial functions and that it is critical to have your immediate environment: home, school or office for exposure.

- Blue light is bad and you should shift to red lights or just take more walks outdoors.

- Teaching your cells to work more efficiently can be achieved by temporarily putting into your body.

- A healthy meal, proper exercise, and meditation will greatly help you achieve maximum brain performance.

Hopefully, applying all these learnings have helped made your more energetic and your overall performance better. Continue following the rules in this program and we guarantee sustained excellent performance for you.

# Final Thoughts

Hey! Did you enjoy this book? We sincerely hope you thoroughly enjoyed this short read and have gotten immensely valuable insights that will help you in any areas of your life.

Would it be too greedy if we ask for a review from you?

It takes 1 minute to leave 1 review to possibly influence 1 more person's decision to read just 1 book which may change their 1 life. Your 1 minute matters and we value it and thank you so much for giving us your 1 minute. If it sucks, just say it sucks. Period.

# FREE BONUS

## P.S. Is it okay if we overdeliver?

Here at Abbey Beathan Publishing, we believe in overdelivering way beyond our reader's expectations. Is it okay if we overdeliver?

Here's the deal, we're going to give you an extremely valuable cheatsheet of "Accelerated Learning". We've partnered up with Ikigai Publishing to present to you the exclusive bonus of "Accelerated Learning Cheatsheet"

What's the catch? We need to trust you... You see, we want to overdeliver and in order for us to do that, we've to trust our reader to keep this bonus a secret to themselves. Why? Because we don't want people to be getting our exclusive accelerated learning cheatsheet without even buying our books itself. Unethical, right?

Ok. Are you ready?

Simply Visit this link: http://bit.ly/acceleratedcheatsheet

We hope you'll enjoy our free bonuses as much as we've enjoyed preparing it for you!

## Free Bonus #2: Free Book Preview of Summary:
## Outliers
## The Book at a Glance

*Outliers: The Story of Success* is critically-acclaimed author and The New Yorker writer Malcolm Gladwell's third best-selling non-fiction book that talks about how people succeed in life through crafted cultural background, impeccable timing and presented opportunities. Published in 2008, the book is compartmentally divided into two parts, the first part talking about opportunities that are presented to successful people and the latter about how legacies can make someone successful. Gladwell carefully examines and narrates how a person's environment, infused with high intensities of motivation and passion affects their possibility of being truly successful and faithfully tells others' success stories often using back-to-back chronologies through the likes of The Beatles, Bill Gates and even the hockey players of The Medicine Hat Tigers. Though *Outliers* fairly abstains from previous books *"The Tipping Point"* and *"Blink"* because of its social narrative, *Outliers* has been praised for being pleasurable to read and might as well have great timing for this generation to understand and comprehend.

Malcolm Timothy Gladwell, born in 1963 in Fareham,

Hampshire, England to Joyce and Graham Gladwell is a staff writer for The New Yorker since 1996 and has written five New York Times Bestseller books, *The Tipping Point: How Little Things Can Make A Big Difference* (2000), *Blink: The Power of Thinking Without Thinking* (2005), *Outliers: The Story of Success* (2008), *What the Dog Saw: And Other Adventures* (2009) and David and *Goliath Underdogs, Misfits, and the Art of Battling Giants* (2013). He also hosts podcast *Revisionist History.*

**The Gladwells moved from England to Canada when the writer was only 6, and graduated at the University of Toronto, Trinity College with a degree in History in 1984. Gladwell worked with Washington Post as a reporter for a decade with articles on science and business before joining the "New Yorker" magazine. He moved to New York shortly after to try his hand at journalism and found international success as a writer and penned all five books to become successful worldwide. Time magazine has named Gladwell as one of its "100 Most Influential People" in 2005 and has received the first "Award for Excellence in the Reporting of Social Issues" by the American Sociological Association in 2007.**

# Introduction

*The Roseto Mystery: "These people were drying of old age. That's it."*

This introduction laboriously introduces us to the Rosetansten men, how they have lived desperately in the mountains of Roseto Valtefore, in a small Italian province of Foggia until such time when they discovered greener pastures in the land across the ocean and moved to America seeking a better life. In Pennsylvania, the Rosetansten men learned how to carry out jobs, work in services and make their way around the city. Led by a priest by the name of Father Pasquale de Nisco, the Rosetansten men were encouraged to plant their own crops, take spiritually enriched lives and build harmonious relationships which would later prove extremely beneficial. Initially called "Little Italy", the citizens of the city renamed it to Roseto, after their origin.

In this overture, Gladwell creatively uses *The Roseto Mystery* to tell the tale of how the residents of Rosetansten men merely had half the rate of heart attack cases in comparison to its neighboring communities. In 1964, a study was published in the Journal of the American Medical Association and examined the reason for the community's near immunity to heart disease and contributed it to the underlying reasons of being a remarkably close-knit community that induced respect and support for another, therefore suggesting that the affirmation of family and social relationships subsidized how a person's personal health would turn out.

Led by physician Stewart Wolf, experts from sociology and medicine came to Roseto to examine and investigate what contributed to the outstanding health of its residents and performed different conclusions ranging from a well-balanced diet, exercise and even good sets of genes. However, this all proved to be counterfactual, as they have found out that the fundamental reason for the outstanding health in the town was due to the peaceful, abetting and close-knit qualities of the community to which Gladwell craftily uses as a debut to his full feature story and herald his book's mission and suffuses his conclusion with that of Stewart Wolf's to prove that success is indeed created and not purely coincidental.

Gladwell creatively uses the Roseto Mystery as a preliminary guide to how this book was going to take its claim, by using the story of the Rosetansten men and giving it a bigger theatre stage. He pushes forward the idea that a little town in Pennsylvania can ward off diseases – even cardiac illnesses just by forming amicable relationships with one another.

In the modern world today, this kind of analysis plays a big role in society as it clears the pathway of an animated discovery into the world of communication and unison amongst humanity, to the point of being immune to major diseases.

# Chapter 1

*The Matthew Effect: "For unto everyone that hath shall be given, and he shall have abundance. But from him that hath not shall be taken away even that which he hath." - Matthew 25:29*

"The Matthew Effect", the first chapter of *Outliers*, where he divides the chapter into six bite-sized bullets, commences with Gladwell's account of the 2007 Memorial Cup hockey championship game between the Medicine Hat Tigers and the Vancouver Giants to which the latter emerged as winners. Gladwell meticulously describes how the game went and effortlessly cites a previous research study performed by Canadian psychologist Dr. Roger Barnsley.

He tells us a story of how Dr. Roger Barnsley and his wife watched a game of hockey, wherein they see these blinking lights that signal a bright idea that leads them to the relative age effect theory Barnsley therefore crafts into a realistic approach.

In this relative age effect theory, Barnsley notices a high percentage of ice-hockey players being born during the first months of the year, from January to March and thoroughly concludes how this greatly affects the performance of a sports team, particularly in the games of hockey, soccer and rugby. In the first chapter of the *Outliers*, Gladwell ceremoniously rides on the idea and creates it as his ticket to show the readers of how age and maturity plays a big role in success. To further rationalize, players born in the early part of the year have a higher chance of being prepared and develop skills faster than those born during the latter part of the year therefore corresponding it to a higher rate of ascendancy. He further explains that being an athlete does not pay attention to dynasty, or money because being in the major league is not something you can easily purchase or is controlled by certain sovereignty. In fact, being an athlete meant you needed to have the ability, the skill, the passion and the dedication to at least render countless of hours training and doing related activities to further enhance your prowess in the field. He creates an imaginary skill pyramid for his readers to conceptualize, where those who participate in this game go up a ladder until they reach the top most part where they find true success.

The second bullet of this chapter begins as Gladwell demonstrates what outliers are; by definition and by how he portrays them, painting an overall view for his readers as he starts to set the stage for the next chapters. He guarantees that as you read and progress throughout his book, he will introduce to you various examples of the different people who have grown into outliers and have become successful. He creates a relatable topic when he describes how regular citizens love to read about tycoons, millionaires, celebrities and follow how their life in the public eye unfolds. He makes a slight jab of irony on how these regular people buy all the articles and autobiographies these famous people make, in an effort to know they made it big and possibly follow suit, enveloped in that dream to become millionaires and billionaires in the sound future. However, in a swift move, Gladwell disputes what is normal to most – which people can rise from nothing and become great. To our author, people become great because of the thousands of hours they spent on perfecting their skill, and eventually becoming an expert in that field. Gladwell goes on to convince his readers that parentage and patronage does have major contributions to a person's success, alluding that a person's environment is vital to his success because internal and external factors do have a sizable impact on a person's wellbeing that eventually transcends to how he performs.

Gladwell also cites two economists Kelly Bedard and Elizabeth Duey who looked into the relationship between scores in Mathematics and Science, contributing to his theory that those born early in the year scored better in comparison to those who were born later in the year. With this, he gives enough justification that although Dr. Barnsley has cited his theory and making athletes as examples, Gladwell advocates that it doesn't only happen in the world of sports, in fact, it happens across all industries, we just don't notice it enough.

He finishes the first chapter going back to the ice-hockey game story and introduces us to Gord Wasden, father of Medicine Hat Tigers player Scott Wasden and how in an interview he has mentioned that his son was born on January 4 – the perfect hockey eligibility, rendering him bigger than kids his age. He ends this chapter with a conclusion that if Scott Wasden was born later in the year, he would have less chance playing in the game and a bigger chance watching from the bench.

CPSIA information can be obtained
at www.ICGtesting.com
Printed in the USA
BVHW041426030919
557429BV00010B/325/P